Actors' Handbook 2010-11

Edited by Simon Dale & Andrew Chapman

a  directory

© Casting Call Pro 2010

This edition first published 2010 by

Casting Call Pro
Unit 1, Waterloo Gardens
Milner Square
London N1 1TY

www.uk.castingcallpro.com

A CIP catalogue record for this book is available from the British Library

ISBN 978-0-9556273-2-3

Set in Frutiger & Serifa
Designed and edited by Andrew Chapman (www.awrc.co.uk)

Printed in Britain by
Polestar Wheatons, Exeter

/continues...

4: Sources of work 157

5: Living as an actor 209

6: Organisations & resources 225

Introduction

Acting can be one of the most rewarding and frustrating of professions. This guide is intended to make your professional life just that little bit easier. With useful introductions to some of the key areas for establishing oneself as a professional actor, and comprehensive listings for agents, service providers, drama schools and useful organisations, the Actors' Handbook is designed to help you pick a path through the ever changing landscape of the professional actor.

Whether you are considering entering the profession, have just taken your first steps, or are already established as an actor, Actors' Handbook is both a useful guide to the industry and an invaluable resource to help further your career development. The 2010-11 Handbook covers topics such as: choosing a drama school; finding work and marketing yourself; auditioning; further training, tax and accountancy for the self-employed actor.

The Actors' Handbook is brought to you by the people behind Casting Call Pro, one of the leading resources for professional UK actors. The information in this book is updated regularly, more recent information can always be found at **www.uk.castingcallpro.com**. This 2010-11 edition has been fully revised, with many extra listings.

If you have any questions about this book or feel an organisation or company ought to be included in future editions please send details to info@blue-compass.com.

Acknowledgements

We are extremely grateful to the following people for their contributions. Each of the contributors bring a fresh and informative insight into what can, at times, seem a daunting and impenetrable industry. Many thanks are due to:

- The National Council for Drama Training (NCDT) – **www.ncdt.co.uk**
- Tim Kent, director of The Actor's Studio – **www.actorsstudio.co.uk**
- Claire Grogan, highly respected headshot photographer – **www.clairegrogan.co.uk**
- Alexander Fodor, director of the Actor's One–Stop Shop, one of the UK's leading showreel providers for both edited clips and shot from scratch – **www.actorsonestopshop.com**
- Kerry Mitchell, director of Cut Glass Productions, specialists in Voice Overs and voicereel production – **www.cutglassproductions.com**
- James Bonallack, director of Foreign Voices, the UK's foremost agency for native foreign language voice over artists and in-house voice over production – **www.foreignvoices.co.uk**
- Hils Barker, acclaimed stand up comic and comedy writer for Radio 4 – **www.hilsbarker.com**.
- Keisha Amponsa Banson, actress and graduate of Mountview Academy of Theatre Arts
- Simon & How Associates, actors' agency founded in 2007 by directors Simon Penn and Samantha How
- TWD Accountants, one of the UK's leading low cost, fixed fee tax accountancy services – **www.twdaccounts.co.uk**

Section 1
Drama schools & training

Choosing a drama school

Do I need to go to drama school?

Training at a reputable drama school is the best route into professional acting. Not only does it afford you an actual grounding in acting and an opportunity to practice your craft, it also gives you credibility in the eyes of casting professionals. (There are a fortunate few who have found success without studying at drama school. They have perhaps been spotted by an agent in an amateur production, but this is a lottery and not to be relied upon if you are serious about making a long-term career in acting.) Attending drama school demonstrates ongoing commitment to your calling and, as long as the school is reputable and you demonstrate a willingness to learn, you'll be better placed at the end of the course to succeed as an actor.

Choosing a course

With so many courses to choose from, it's vital to do your research before applying. Start by looking at the institution itself: is it a university or college dedicated to drama, media or stage craft? or a private collection of teachers operating out of rented premises? How long has the institution has been established and how long it has been offering a drama course? It is also important to look at who is teaching the course: do the teachers have the experience required to teach you what you need to succeed? Take time to review what facilities the institution offers: do they have their own theatre? Do they put on end of your showcases and if so how well attended are they – eg do they get good agents coming along, do they have a track record of finding agency representation? As well as the prestige of a school, location and funding may be important to you. While the majority of schools are in London there also schools in Wales, Scotland and throughout England. Crucially, check the institution's pedigree by researching past students – where are they now?

Along with your choice of institution, your course selection is also pivotal. Many courses will offer a broad cross-section of acting disciplines, while others are more specific, eg dedicated to screen acting or stage acting. A school's website should give you a good idea of the courses they offer – look thoroughly at the course outline and if you have any questions give the school a call; they'll be happy to help with your enquiries. When choosing a course, there are a number of factors to consider. Your research should include finding out about a course's reputation by talking to people and gleaning what you can from industry publications and the Internet (don't just go by the school's website which might have an inherent bias). Remember, the reputation of any particular course will fluctuate over time depending on its output of actors and its current teaching staff.

Entry is based mainly on auditions, for which you will usually be expected to select two speeches (one modern, one classical) and for which you may well be charged an audition fee (usually around £30 to £50). You will be expected to cover your own travel and accommodation costs to attend auditions. Don't forget to check the deadlines for applications and do expect competition for places to be extremely high.

With so many factors to weigh up, choosing the right drama school can be a daunting process. A good starting point is to look at the Conference of Drama Schools (CDS) member list. The CDS comprises Britain's twenty-two leading Drama Schools. CDS exists in order to set and maintain the highest standards of training within the vocational drama sector, and to make it easier for prospective students to understand the range of courses on offer and the application process. Schools often run a number of courses, so you then have to do your homework and assess which course best suits your interests and long term goals. The National Council for Drama Training (NCDT) accredits those courses which it feels offer the highest levels of vocational training. The National Council for Drama Training is the body charged by the industry with overseeing and safeguarding professional training standards for actors, stage managers and technicians in the UK. Panels composed of industry professionals inspect courses on a five-yearly basis to bestow accreditation on courses in the performing arts which the Council considers offer a high level of professional relevance and quality. The NCDT provides a list of accredited courses in acting, musical theatre, stage management and technical production and a useful Guide to Training offering comprehensive guidance on different types of training and how it is funded. As well as the NCDT accredited courses, there are plenty of schools, including CDS members, which run well regarded courses but which don't, for different reasons, have NCDT accreditation.

What if I've had no other training or acting experience?

There are no formal criteria you must meet in order apply to a drama school. Fundamentally, what the schools are looking for is genuine talent and commitment. That said, while you are not required to have acted at school or in local amateur theatre, it certainly won't do you any harm in the eyes of casting directors, and amateur theatre can be a good way of learning more about the craft and gaining valuable experience.

Training for under 18s?

For those too young to be eligible for three-year drama school courses, the traditional route is stage school, where a range of acting, singing and dance skills is likely to be taught. Most of these are private and therefore there will be considerable fees to meet, although there may be some scholarship options. There are a few publicly funded stage schools and a number of part-time options.

Another option for younger children to discover whether acting is really for them is to attend a drama workshop or group. The National Association of Youth Theatres (**www.nayt.org.uk**) and the National Youth Theatre (**www.nyt.org.uk**) will help you track down suitable workshops and youth theatre groups. If you are in Ireland have a look at the National Association for Youth Drama (www.youthdrama.ie) and if you're in Scotland check out the Scottish Youth Theatre (www.scottishyouththeatre.org)

Training for older actors

As with any degree-level course, most people taking it are likely to be in their late teens or twenties – but that doesn't mean there aren't opening for mature. Schools are generally very receptive to older applicants as they can bring life experience to bear in the acting process. As Sartre said, "Acting is a question of absorbing other people's personalities and adding some of your own experience." No bad thing, then, to have a bit of life experience under your belt. Many people decide to retrain or have a career shift and the older actor may even be better able to finance their training. Also, many young actors leave the profession in the first few years for one reason or another, so there may be a little less competition for work.

Check with the drama school, though – some do have age limits. Even if they don't, steel yourself for being thrown into the society of people considerably younger than yourself. If you can't find a suitable full-time course, a part-time one may be worth considering, though these are less likely to lead to career openings afterwards.

Training for actors with disabilities

There's a growing demand for actors from a broader and more inclusive spectrum of society, so disability need not be an inherent barrier to an acting career (though opportunities may still be fewer). Check with the main drama schools what their policy is – and of course what the facilities there are like for disabled people, such as hearing loops for deaf people in auditoria or rehearsal spaces, ramps for wheelchairs and so on.

The National Disability Arts Forum (**www.ndaf.org**) may be able to help with general advice, both on finding training and work as well as overcoming any potential discrimination.

There are numerous theatre companies which either welcome or specialise in employing actors with disabilities. Some of these – such as Graeae (**www.graeae.org**) and Mind the Gap (**www.mind-the-gap.org.uk**) – themselves run training courses and are building links with drama schools to improve access to training for disabled people.

Applying

Applying for a course entails contacting the school, via its website, by telephone or in writing, in order to get your hands on an application form and prospectus. A standard application form will ask for your basic details, your acting experience to date and your reasons for wanting to attend the course. Check the deadline for applications as these vary from course to course and school to school. Don't leave it until the last minute – get the application in as early as you can! There's nothing to stop you from applying for more than one course, though if you've received a place on one it's polite to let the other(s) know. There should be no fees for applying, but you should bear in mind that if you're called for an audition a school will usually charge an audition fee.

The course itself

Once you've secured your place on a course you can give yourself a pat on the back, and then get ready for the hard work: fame costs. Okay, so you might not be looking for fame, but you get the point. If you're going to get the most out of the course (for which you'll be paying either directly or indirectly), you can't rest on your laurels. This isn't the quick route to celebrity and the paparazzi.

You will be expected to attend classes, prepare, rehearse, study, and to exercise self-discipline, commitment and organisation. You'll be working with respected teachers and alongside other talented actors who will go on to work in the industry and whose path you will cross time and time again in the coming years. So take the time to look, listen and learn.

Acting courses emphasise the practical exploration of theatre, with classes revolving around physical exercises, roleplays and scenarios leading to full productions, though every course will be backed up with lectures about the history and theory of acting.

Foundation courses

Some schools and a growing number of organisations offer foundation or 'taster' courses. These can be short-term, part-time or intensive courses designed to give you an introduction to acting. It can help to have completed a foundation course before applying for drama school but they shouldn't be viewed as a substitute for a full-time drama course. You should be wary of courses promising too much for a short investment of your time and a large investment of your money. As with all other courses, check out the credibility of the institution, teachers and facilities before parting with any money.

Drama school funding

Drama school training doesn't come cheap. In addition to tuition fees (which will run into the £1,000s), you'll also have to fund course materials, accommodation, travel and living expenses. If the course is in London, as most are, you should factor in additional costs for day-to-day living expenses. Rent, in particular, is more expensive in London than other regions, not to mention the general cost of living.

Remember, on graduation you won't be guaranteed a lucrative West End contact, and even if you get an agent from your end of year showcase you could find yourself facing considerable ongoing costs. Headshots can cost up to £300, putting together a showreel may cost an additional £300, putting on a showcase can cost another £300 and finding out about jobs through The Stage, PCR, Casting Call Pro and other services can cost you an additional £500 per year, not to mention the cost of Spotlight and Equity. That's not to say you will need to bear all these costs, but it's worth building some flexibility into your finances to ensure you can survive those tough first months after graduation.

Student Loans
Student Loans are indexed to the rate of inflation and do not have to be paid back until you have graduated and your income is over £15,000 pa. They are available to eligible full-time higher education students; two types of loan cover fees and maintenance respectively.

For maintenance loans, for the year 2010/11 the maximum loan is £5, 067 for students living away from home outside London, and more for those living away from home and based in London. Eligible students are automatically entitled to 75% of the maximum, with the remainder dependent on an assessment of the student's and their household's income. The amounts are reduced in the final year of study to take into account the shorter year. For up-to-date details check the government's student finance information pages at: www.direct.gov.uk/en/EducationAndLearning
Maintenance grants

If you're from a low income household you may also be eligible for a maintenance grant from the government. These are worth up to £2,906 for the 2010/11 academic year and do not have to be paid back. Again, see **www.direct.gov.uk** for more information about these and other possible sources of funding.

Bursaries and scholarships

Many schools have their own bursary and scholarship schemes which will vary from full course fees and some help towards living expenses to smaller awards which will go some but not all the way to covering your costs. There will only be a limited number of bursaries/scholarships given out each year, and competition will be tough, so you certainly can't rely on, or expect to receive, this kind of financial support. Check out the funding policy and opportunities for each establishment thoroughly before applying.

Charities and other sources

It is also possible to raise funds from charities, trusts and foundations – a list of these is available in a factsheet at the NCDT website: **www.ncdt.co.uk/guidetotraining/funding**

If you are going down this route, make sure you target suitable sources of funding carefully and avoid simply sending out a standard letter to as many organisations as you can get addresses for. Your application will stand much more of a chance if you've tailored it to an appropriate body, and in an individual manner. Another route might be to think of local businesses who have shown evidence of supporting the arts – check out local newspapers and theatres to see which sponsors' logos appear, and make contact with them.

Other ideas if funding is a problem

If you're concerned about the costs of further training you could choose to team up with other actors to read through plays or replay old drama school exercises. In addition, take time to read as many plays and scripts as possible, and catch innovative shows performed by professionals and your peers. Watching others perform will keep your ideas fresh which may be useful at your next audition. The crucial thing is to view acting as a career that requires ongoing support and development.

Funding: Useful links & organisations

STUDENT LOANS COMPANY
{T} 0800 40 50 10
WWW.SLC.CO.UK

HOT COURSES FUNDING SEARCH
WWW.SCHOLARSHIP-SEARCH.ORG.UK

STUDENTS AWARDS AGENCY FOR SCOTLAND
WWW.SAAS.GOV.UK

STUDENT FINANCE WALES
WWW.STUDENTFINANCEWALES.CO.UK

Courses: Useful links & organisations

NATIONAL COUNCIL FOR DRAMA TRAINING (NCDT)
www.ncdt.co.uk | 020 7407 3686
Visit the NCDT's website for a full list of accredited drama courses and to download a copy of their Applicants' Guide to Auditioning and Interviewing at Dance and Drama School or the Guide to Vocational Training in Dance and Drama.

CONFERENCE OF DRAMA SCHOOLS (CDS)
www.drama.ac.uk | info@cds.drama.ac.uk

COURSES, CAREERS – WHY CHOOSE DRAMA SCHOOL?
www.he.courses-careers.com/drama.htm

CASTING CALL PRO - COMPREHENSIVE LIST OF SCHOOLS
www.uk.castingcallpro.com/college.php

PART-TIME COURSES
www.ncdt.co.uk/parttime.asp

LEARN DIRECT – ACTORS
www.learndirect-advice.co.uk

THE NATIONAL DISABILITY ARTS FORUM
www.ndaf.org

DISABILITY ARTS ONLINE
www.disabilityartsonline.org.uk | info@disabilityartsonline.org.uk

A-Z of drama schools & colleges

(These schools are all members of the Conference of Drama Schools. An asterisk * next to a course denotes that is NCDT accredited. Please note that where student numbers per course and deadlines for application are given, these are approximate and may vary from year to year.)

ARTS EDUCATIONAL SCHOOL LONDON

14 BATH ROAD
CHISWICK
LONDON W4 1LY
{T} 020 8987 6655
DRAMA@ARTSED.CO.UK
WWW.ARTSED.CO.UK
COURSES: BA (HONS) ACTING, 3 YEARS (100 STUDENTS)
MA ACTING, 1 YEAR (30 STUDENTS)
BA (HONS) MUSICAL THEATRE, 3 YEARS (130 STUDENTS) *
BA PERFORMANCE STUDIES / (POST GRADUATE DIPLOMA) 1 YEAR (130 STUDENTS) *
DEADLINE: END OF JUNE

The School of Acting offer contemporary, industry-relevant vocational training for actors. It equips the student to a high level for a career as a professional actor in a range of performance contexts including live performance, film, television and radio. The School of Acting works to create an environment for training, which is based on trust , mutual respect and passion. The school believes that it is from within this environment that students will be secure enough to take risks. In addition, the school believes that the individual performer learns best from within the group, and that the theatre ensemble grows from the constructive input of every individual.

ALRA
(ACADEMY OF LIVE AND RECORDED ARTS)

STUDIO 1, THE ROYAL PATRIOTIC BUILDING
FITSHUGH GROVE
LONDON SW18 3SX
{T} 020 8870 6475
INFO@ALRA.CO.UK
WWW.ALRA.CO.UK
COURSES: BA (HONS) ACTING, 3 YEARS (42 STUDENTS)
MA ACTING, 15 MONTHS (28 STUDENTS)
DEADLINE: C. 1ST MAY

The courses are designed to give you adaptability, flexibility and openness needed to sustain a career in the stage and screen industry, you will explore fully and progressively your creative, vocal and physical potential. We will instill yin you the self-discipline the industry expects of you. You will be shown current working methods and practices to enable you to work effectively and professional practitioners from all areas of the industry and you will receive lectures and workshops on the practical business of being an actor.

BIRMINGHAM SCHOOL OF ACTING (BSSD)
G2 – MILLENNIUM POINT
CURZON STREET
BIRMINGHAM B4 7XG
{T} 0121 331 7220
INFO@BSA.UCE.AC.UK
WWW.BSA.UCE.AC.UK
COURSES: BA (HONS) ACTING, 3 YEARS *
PG DIP / MA ACTING, 1 YEAR *
Birmingham School Of Acting is a small, specialist institution with 134 full time students on its two undergraduate acting courses and a staff of more than 60 working professionals. Birmingham School of Acting is a faculty of UCE Birmingham (University of Central England) and is accredited by the National Council of Drama Training (NCDT)

BRISTOL OLD VIC THEATRE SCHOOL
2 DOWNSIDE ROAD
BRISTOL BS8 2XF
ENQUIRIES@OLDVIC.AC.UK
WWW.OLDVIC.AC.UK
COURSES: BA (HONS) ACTING, 3 YEARS (12 STUDENTS) *
FOUNDATION DIPLOMA IN ACTING, 2 YEARS (14 STUDENTS) *
CERT HE ACTING, 1 YEAR (4 STUDENTS) *
ACTING FOR OVERSEAS STUDENTS, 1 YEAR (12 STUDENTS) *
DEADLINE: 1ST MARCH
Opened by Laurence Olivier in 1946, the school is an industry-led vocational training establishment preparing students for careers in acting, stage management, costume, design, scenic art, directing, theatre arts management, production management, lighting, electrics, sound, studio management, propmaking, VT editing and scenic construction. Work encompasses the breadth of theatre, television, radio, film, recording, events and trade presentations and the ever-increasing areas of employment open to a trained workforce in arts and entertainment.

CENTRAL SCHOOL OF SPEECH AND DRAMA
EMBASSY THEATRE
ETON AVENUE
LONDON NW3 3HY
{T} 020 7722 8183
ENQUIRIES@CSSD.AC.UK
WWW.CSSD.AC.UK
COURSES: BA (HONS) ACTING, 3 YEARS (54 STUDENTS) *
BA (HONS) DRAMA, APPLIED THEATRE AND EDUCATION (66 STUDENTS) *
MA ACTING, 1 YEAR (18 STUDENTS)
MA ACTING FOR SCREEN, 1 YEAR (18 STUDENTS)
MA ACTOR TRAINING AND COACHING, 1 YEAR (14 STUDENTS)
DEADLINE: 15TH JANUARY
Founded in 1906 by Elsie Fogerty to offer an entirely new form of training in speech and drama for young actors and other students. The choice of name – the Central School – highlighted the school's commitment to a broad range of training systems for vocal and dramatic performance. It espoused principles that were firmly held yet responsive to change. That sense of continuing critical openness to new development is a lasting hallmark of the school.

CYGNET TRAINING THEATRE
NEW THEATRE
FRIARS GATE
EXETER EX2 4AZ
{T} 01392 277189
CYGNETARTS@BTCONNECT.COM
WWW.CYGNETNEWTHEATRE.COM
COURSES: PROFESSIONAL ACTING COURSE, 3
YEARS (6 STUDENTS)
DEADLINE: NONE
Formal training in voice, movement, music, dance and video film are all part of the daily work of the company but rehearsal and performance remain strong features of the experience-based training. Intensive short courses are built in to the training for Stage Fighting and Radio Techniques First year actors play small parts proceeding via medium roles during the second year to leading roles chosen to give them the best possible showcase during the third year.

DRAMA CENTRE LONDON
CENTRAL SAINT MARTINS COLLEGE
SOUTHAMPTON ROW
LONDON WC1B 4AP
{T} 020 7267 1177
INFO@CSM.ARTS.AC.UK
WWW.CSM.ARTS.AC.UK/DRAMA
Courses: BA (Hons) Acting, 3 years
Drama Centre London offers its students a unique blend of training methods. As part of Central Saint Martins College of Art and Design and the University of the Arts London, Drama Centre provides an international outlook, a central London location and excellent learning and performance facilities. They make studying at the Drama Centre a profound, enjoyable and rewarding experience. Our courses are intended to enable you to develop a clear understanding of yourself as a creative person and therefore our students are distinguished by their flair, maturity and commitment.

DRAMA STUDIO LONDON
GRANGE COURT
1 GRANGE ROAD, EALING
LONDON W5 5QN
{T} 020 8579 3897
ADMIN@DRAMASTUDIOLONDON.CO.UK
WWW.DRAMASTUDIOLONDON.CO.UK
Courses: PG Dip in Acting, 1 year (60 students) *
PG Dip in Acting, 2 years (24 students)
Deadline: None
Drama Studio London fully prepares you for life in the real world of today's professional theatre. The training is passionate, personal and always relevant. Our intention is not just to teach you how to act. It is to teach you how to be an actor. The student and staff community at Drama Studio London is a family, with all the encouragement, friendship and competition this means. Through their commitment and hard work most students find work within weeks of graduation. Our teachers, directors and administrators are among the best the profession has to offer, drawn from theatre, film, television, radio and the business side of the entertainment industry.

EAST 15 ACTING SCHOOL
HATFIELDS, RECTORY LANE
LOUGHTON
ESSEX IG10 3RY
{T} 020 8508 5983
EAST15@ESSEX.AC.UK
WWW.EAST15.AC.UK
COURSES: BA (HONS) ACTING, 3 YEARS (32 STUDENTS) *
BA ACTING AND CONTEMPORARY THEATRE, 1 YEAR (32 STUDENTS) *
MA ACTING (FILM / TV), 1 YEAR (16 STUDENTS) *
MA ACTING, 1 YEAR (32 STUDENTS) *
DEADLINE: POST-GRADUATE – NONE
UNDERGRADUATE – END OF MAY

East 15 grew from the work of Joan Littlewood's famed Theatre Workshop. Much of the Littlewood approach was based upon the theories of Stanislavski, and the company inherited the socially committed spirit of the Unity Theatre movement, which brought many new voices into British Theatre for the first time. Theatre Workshop broke new ground, re-interpreting the classics for a modern age, commissioning new plays from socially committed writers, and creating an ensemble capable of inventing new work, such as the new legendary Oh What A Lovely War. Littlewood created a wonderful ensemble, who combined inspired, improvisational brilliance with method, technique, research, text, analysis, and the expression of real emotions. Over the years, new training methods were evolved to strip actors of affectations, attitudes, ego trips, etc. The quest was always the search for the truth: for oneself, the character, the text.

GUILFORD SCHOOL OF ACTING (GSA)
MILLMEAD TERRACE
GUILDFORD
SURREY GU2 4YT
{T} 01483 560701
ENQUIRIES@CONSERVATOIRE.ORG
WWW.CONSERVATOIRE.ORG
COURSES: BA (HONS) ACTING, 3 YEARS (57 STUDENTS) *
NATIONAL DIPLOMA IN ACTING, 3 YEARS
ACTING DIPLOMA, 1 YEAR (8 STUDENTS) *
PG DIP / MA MUSICAL THEATRE, 1 YEAR (20 STUDENTS)
BA (HONS) MUSICAL THEATRE, 3 YEARS (128 STUDENTS) *
NATIONAL DIPLOMA IN MUSICAL THEATRE, 3 YEARS
DEADLINE: 31ST JANUARY

From The Moment you start at the Conservatoire to the moment you graduate will be the most challenging time of your life. Training for the profession is as tough as training to compete in the Olympics. We have to prepare you for the competition you will meet one you have graduated. The course is designed to get the best out of you and to encourage you to be versatile in your skills. We concentrate on training the whole person. Our job is to improve your strengths and tackle your weaknesses with you and our overall aim is to help you become versatile as an actor who can sing, dance, work on musicals or straight plays or even in television and radio; all your classes connect to that aim. Acting is the core to all that we do and idea behind your training is that the techniques you learn mean that you can act through singing and dancing as well as through scripts for the stage, television, film or radio.

GUILDHALL SCHOOL OF MUSIC AND DRAMA
SILK STREET
BARBICAN
LONDON EC2Y 8DT
{T} 020 7628 2571
DRAMA@GSMD.AC.UK
WWW.GSMD.AC.UK
COURSES: BA (HONS) ACTING, 3 YEARS (24 STUDENTS) *
MA ACTING, 3 YEARS (24 STUDENTS)
MA TRAINING ACTORS (VOICE) OR (MOVEMENT), 2 YEARS, PART-TIME (4 STUDENTS)
DEADLINE: ACTING – MID-JANUARY
TRAINING ACTORS – MAY
The modern Guildhall School is distinctive in being the only major European conservatoire which is both a music school and a drama school, and one which is preeminent in technical theatre, professional development and music therapy. The acting programme is highly regarded in the profession for the thoroughness of its audition processes, the passion, quality and rigour of its teaching, its emphasis on the integration of craft training , the

care and attention for the individual development of each student and the strong ensemble ethic shared by staff and students.

ITALIA CONTI ACADEMY OF THEATRE ARTS
AVONDALE
72 LANDOR ROAD
LONDON SW9 9PH
{T} 020 7733 3210
ACTING@LSBU.AC.UK
WWW.ITALIACONTI-ACTING.CO.UK
COURSES: BA (HONS) ACTING, 3 YEARS (25-30 STUDENTS) *
DEADLINE: MID-MAY
Italia Conti Academy of Theatre Arts is a world-renowned centre for actor training. Its graduates populate the performance industries and it is this commercial edge that makes the BA (Hons) Acting course unique. It is one of the country's leading vocational acting courses with an emphasis on professional development and employability. We believe that acting is not just an art form but also a craft and our students leave the course equipped with the skills necessary to take up meaningful roles within the profession.

LIVERPOOL INSTITUTE OF PERFORMING ARTS (LIPA)

MOUNT STREET
LIVERPOOL
L1 9HF
{T}0151 330 3000
ADMISSIONS@LIPA.AC.UK
WWW.LIPA.AC.UK
COURSES: BA (HONS) ACTING (PERFORMING ARTS), 3 YEARS (STUDENTS)
DEADLINE:

The Liverpool Institute for Performing Arts opened in 1996 to forge a new approach to performing arts training. It was co-founded by our Lead Patron Sir Paul McCartney and Mark Featherstone-Witty (LIPA's Principal), and is housed in his old school, which underwent a multi-million pound renovation to transform it into a state-of-the-art performing arts higher education institution. Today LIPA has a reputation for being one of the UK's leading higher education institutions. LIPA provides education and training in performing arts, theatre and performance design and technology and management disciplines in a hands-on, collaborative environment.

LONDON ACADEMY OF MUSIC AND DRAMATIC ART

155 TALGARTH ROAD
LONDON W14 9DA
{T} 020 8834 0500
ENQUIRIES@LAMDA.ORG.UK
WWW.LAMDA.ORG.UK
COURSES: BA (HONS) ACTING, 3 YEARS (30 STUDENTS) *

BA (HONS) ACTING, 2 YEARS (30 STUDENTS)
PG DIP CLASSICAL ACTING, 1 YEAR (C. 20 STUDENTS)
DEADLINE: 1ST MARCH

LAMDA is an independent drama school, dedicated to the vocational training of actors, stage managers and technicians, directors and designers in the skills and levels of creativity necessary to meet the highest demands and best opportunities in theatre, film, radio and TV. The group work ethic is central to LAMDA's teaching. The training does not deconstruct the student in order to rebuild a LAMDA product but encourages and develops innate skills. The courses are practical not academic. Class times are Monday - Friday 9am - 5.30pm with some evening and weekend classes. All classes are compulsory.

MANCHESTER METROPOLITAN UNIVERSITY SCHOOL OF THEATRE

MABEL TYLECOTE BUILDING
CAVENDISH STREET
MANCHESTER M15 6BG
{T} 0161 247 1305
ENQUIRIES@MMU.AC.UK
COURSES: BA (HONS) ACTING, 3 YEARS (25 STUDENTS) *
MA ACTING, 1 YEAR (C. 12 STUDENTS)
DEADLINE: MAY

The Manchester School of Theatre at the Manchester Metropolitan University has a long standing international reputation for preparing students for careers as professional actors. We have a range of courses

on offer, including undergraduate, post-graduate and short courses.
Our graduates have found careers in all of the major theatre, film and TV companies including the BBC, ITV, the Royal National Theatre, the Royal Shakespeare Company as well as all of the major touring and regional repertory companies.

MOUNTVIEW ACADEMY OF THEATRE ARTS

1 KINGFISHER PLACE
CLARENDON ROAD
LONDON
N22 6XF
{T} 020 8881 2201
ENQUIRIES@MOUNTVIEW.ORG.UK
WWW.MOUNTVIEW.ORG.UK
COURSES: BA (HONS) ACTING, 3 YEARS *
PG DIP ACTING, 1 YEAR *
DEADLINE: BA – 1ST MARCH
PG - 30TH JUNE
Founded in 1945, Mountview is now recognised as one of the country's leading Academies of Theatre Arts, offering an extensive and stimulating training for those interested in pursuing performance, directing, or technical theatre careers. Mountview's courses are structures to give students a thorough grounding in all aspects of their chosen field. Our students are trained to a high level to develop a range of skills which will enable them to bring thought, energy and commitment to their profes-sional work, giving them the tools to succeed in a competitive industry.

OXFORD SCHOOL OF DRAMA

SANSOMES FARM STUDIOS
WOODSTOCK OX20 1ER
{T} 01993 812883
INFO@OXFORDDRAMA.AC.UK
WWW.OXFORDDRAMA.AC.UK
COURSES: DIPLOMA IN ACTING, 3 YEARS (18 STUDENTS) *
ACTING, 1 YEAR (18 STUDENTS) *
DEADLINE: END OF MAY
The Oxford School of Drama has achieved phenomenal success over the past 22 years. It is the youngest of the accredited drama schools and is dedicated to providing outstanding vocational training for actors. We offer practical, hands-on training to talented students who are committed to forging careers as actors. In order that we are able to provide the best possible training we have decided not to run degree courses. This means that we don't have pressures put upon us to increase our number of students or courses as is so often the case in drama schools which enter into partnership with a university.

QUEEN MARGARET UNIVERSITY COLLEGE

QUEEN MARGARET UNIVERSITY
EDINBURGH EH21 6UU
{T} 0131 317 3247
DRAMAADMIN@QMU.AC.UK
WWW.QMUC.AC.UK
COURSES: BA (HONS) DRAMA AND
PERFORMANCE, 3-4 YEARS (65 – 70 STUDENTS)
*

The School offers a dynamic programme of training geared towards professional work in the arts and entertainment industries and a lively and inquisitive practical study of contemporary theatre and links with the industry are strong. In both undergraduate and postgraduate education, the aim is to develop graduates who are critical and reflective independent practitioners and are immediately employable within the theatre and performance sectors. Furthermore, as a School we believe that it is vital that our work reflects contemporary working practice and therefore, where appropriate, students collaborate across programmes on a variety of projects.

ROSE BRUFORD COLLEGE

LAMORBEY PARK
BURNT OAK LANE
SIDCUP DA15 9DF
{T} 020 83082600
ENQUIRIES@BRUFORD.AC.UK
WWW.BRUFORD.AC.UK
COURSES: BA (HONS) ACTING, 3 YEARS (14
STUDENTS) *

DEADLINE: 15TH JANUARY
At the heart of all work at Rose Bruford College is a spirit of collaboration. We embrace the broadest range of performing arts and skills-based training, providing an educational experience that offers all students the breadth of transferable skills and the depth of knowledge required to be successful in a rapidly changing world. What binds all students together is their passionate determination to make their own innovative – sometimes radical – impact on the communal world of theatre and performance.

ROYAL ACADEMY OF DRAMATIC ARTS (RADA)

62-64 GOWER STREET
LONDON WC1E 6ED
{T} 020 7636 7076
ENQUIRIES@RADA.AC.UK
WWW.RADA.AC.UK
COURSES: BA (HONS) ACTING, 3 YEARS (28
STUDENTS) *
DEADLINE: 1ST MARCH
Our students frequently achieve overnight success, but that is not our goal: we want our graduates still to be applying their RADA-training years after they have left us. We've been training first class theatre-makers for over a hundred years, but we haven't stopped inquiring how we can do it better. Our teachers draw upon their experience of the past and present to give our students the expertise to shape the

drama of tomorrow. We cannot give you the desire to be the best in your field, but if you have it our staff will help you nurture, focus and refine it.

ROYAL SCOTTISH ACADEMY OF MUSIC AND DRAMA

100 RENFREW STREET
GLASGOW G2 3DB
{T} 0141 332 4101
DRAMAADMISSIONS@RSAMD.AC.UK
WWW.RSAMD.AC.UK
COURSES: BA ACTING, 3 YEARS (24 STUDENTS) *
DEADLINE: MID JANUARY

The School of Drama is a dynamic, leading edge place of training and development for emergent artists. It is one of the UK's premiere schools and has a rapidly evolving international profile. It aims to nurture and promote the development of artists of excellence, enabling them to pursue fruitful and meaningful careers in a national and international context, thereby making a contribution to the cultural landscapes.

THE ROYAL WELSH COLLEGE OF MUSIC AND DRAMA

CATHAYS PARK
CARDIFF CF10 3ER
{T} 029 2039 1327
DRAMA.ADMISSIONS@RWCMD.AC.UK
WWW.RWCMD.AC.UK
COURSES: BA (HONS) ACTING, 3 YEARS (20 STUDENTS) *
PG ACTING FOR STAGE, SCREEN AND RADIO, 1 YEAR (10 STUDENTS) *
DEADLINE: BA - 15TH JANUARY
PG - 1ST MARCH

The Royal Welsh College of Music and Drama is the National Conservatoire of Wales and a leading UK provider of specialist practical and performance-based training in music and drama. We provide training that will enable our students to discover and develop their own artistic individuality and to not only to enter the music, theatre and related professions but to shape the future of those professions. Our dedicated teachers have a wealth of professional experience and the College collaborates with a number of high-profile arts organizations, visiting artists and directors to ensure that the unique vocational nature of our training programmes reflect the current practices and conditions of the professional world.

Section 2
Agents

The agent's role

If casting directors (see the next chapter for more about them) are the doorways to the acting world then casting agents are the keys. While it is not obligatory to get an agent, it is advisable. They will work alongside you to help you develop a financially stable and fulfilling career. They will be privy to casting information that isn't available to the public, even on specialized casting websites. Good agents will put you forward for suitable upcoming auditions (often not publicly advertised) and protect your interests, negotiating the best deal for you, handling contracts, collecting fees, managing your diary, and fighting your corner if anything goes wrong. Basically, they allow you to focus on your acting while they look after the business side of your career. (Though it will be up to you to handle your personal finances and, as a self-employer actor, to file your Annual Return – see the separate section in Tax & Accountancy.)

What does an agent do?
In a nutshell, they find you work, negotiate contracts and collect fees on your behalf. In return, they take a commission (usually 10-20%) from work they find you. Their primary role is to put you forward for castings and help get you work - to raise your profile and maximise the number of auditions and interviews you are considered for. Privy to opportunities that are generally kept out of the public realm, they have close relationships with the all-important casting directors.

The other important role of an agent is to negotiate and collect fees on your behalf. Your agent should know the market rate for a particular production and the business of reaching an agreed fee should be their area of expertise. They will also be responsible for the contract itself. Not only will they be working on your behalf to get you the best deal (and their own, because of course they are dependent on the commission they make from you for their own living), they will be saving you from having to go through the often tricky nitty-gritty of fees and contracts, freeing you to concentrate on the main job in hand – the actual acting.

There should be no joining fee for signing-up with an agency, so be wary of those who try to get you to part with any money up front. The actors' union Equity advises against signing up with anyone who asks for money at this stage.

Most agents work on a sole representation basis – ie you're represented only by that one agent. It is not uncommon for some agencies to work in a specialist sector – eg commercials. In those instances actors may have a main agent and then a secondary agent for the specialist sector. Any work you get (whether through the agent or your own networking and contacts) will be subject to commission, which varies from agency to agency. The rate of commission is generally between 10% and 20% – but remember that larger agencies, and indeed the more successful smaller ones, will also charge VAT on top of that.

No matter how much you resent seeing a slice of your earnings being given over to the Inland Revenue and a further slice to your agent, especially if it's acting work you've got through your own efforts rather than via the agent, don't try to hoodwink them by withholding details of acting work to avoid commission. This is a rocky road that's likely to lead to the break-up of the partnership.

Some agencies will give you a contract to sign. Make sure you read it through properly and, if you're happy, sign two copies, keeping one for yourself. An important part of the contract to look out for is the notice period for leaving an agency – there may be a period where you have left but are still obliged to pay commission, so check the details carefully.

Getting an agent

Ask fellow actors (and teachers if you have attended a drama course) for recommendations and tips; check websites; view agency websites (see if they are open to new clients or if their lists are closed) and utilise all the resources at your disposal e.g. the Casting Call Pro agency directory – **www.uk.castingcallpro.com/asearch.php** – and that of The Agents' Association, **www.agents-uk.com**). Agencies vary from the giants such as Independent (formerly ICM) with hundreds of prestigious clients, many of them high profile, household names, to much smaller ones with a staff of only one or two and a client list of perhaps a few dozen. Think about whether the size of the agency matters to you: larger ones are likely to have a greater reach, but may not be able to spare time for prolonged personal contact with clients. Conversely, a smaller agency can make you feel more cared for – but have fewer contacts. Either way, always be friendly in your dealings with the agency and get to know the staff.

Once you've drawn up your target shortlist, write to the agencies with a covering letter, your CV and a professional black and white photograph. Write your name and contact details on the back of the photograph, too. Don't email the agency unless they specifically invite it, and avoid phoning unless to check whether they are currently taking on new clients.

It is helpful, though more time-consuming, to tailor your approach to individual agents (see the advice writing a covering letter in Section 3). Address your letter to a specific person – contact names are listed in the directory of agents after this chapter. Be straight-to-the-point (without being rude) in your letter. Ensure you check the postage required before sending your package as a CV, headshot and cover letter will require more than just a standard 1st class stamp. No agency will thank you for obliging them to pay a shortfall in the postage!

In your covering letter explain why you feel this agency is right for you and highlight any upcoming showcases or productions you'll be performing in, should the agent wish to see you on stage. Be aware that due to the sheer volume of interest they receive, and because their main responsibility is to their existing clients, agents can't see every production, so be patient and don't be put off by a standard 'our lists are full' reply.

There is a limit on the number of actors an agent can represent. For this reason they are careful about whom they represent and will be looking for actors whom they believe show potential and will be successful. Depending on their existing client list, they may feel they have reached capacity in certain areas (eg age, look etc.), though most agents would be willing to take on an extra client if they feel they have exceptional talent. In your letter, mention that you can supply a showreel on request.

An agent may respond by saying that you look interesting but are not suitable at that particular time (for a variety of reasons), but to keep in touch. This is sound advice: you can send an updated CV and headshot every now and then to keep you on their radar (but make sure you don't badger them to the point of irritation!).

Keep sending out letters and working your contacts. It can be dispiriting but if you're deterred by this initial rejection you have a long road ahead of you when it comes to casting auditions. Representation and roles may not come immediately, but that's not to say it won't happen. Your watchwords should be self-belief and perseverance.

Some agencies may expect you to come for an interview before they take you on – as always, dress smartly and be confident without being pushy, and turn up on time!

The actor/agent relationship

The relationship between an agent and an actor is vital to the ongoing success of the partnership. Dialogue is the key to a good working relationship with your agent. A good agent will let you know what they're putting you forward for and may also be able to offer you advice and give you post-audition feedback from the casting director. Equally, you should let an agent know how a casting went. The more feedback you give them, the better you can plan ahead and prepare for future castings.

There will be, unless you're very lucky, periods of unemployment during which you may be tearing your hair out. It's natural to wonder if your agent is doing all they can for you and to question your representation. Remember, though, that this is the nature of the industry you've chosen. Agents can sing your praises and get you a foot in the door but after that it's up to you. The truth is that many, many actors may be put forward and considered for a role, but the part will be given to only one. That you don't get a part is not the fault of your agent.

If you feel you're simply not being put forward for things and are effectively lying dormant on your agent's books then it's a good idea to raise this with them. In many cases your concerns will be addressed and allayed. (It's not in an agent's interest to ignore you – an out of work actor brings no revenue!) In some cases there may be a parting of the ways, mutual or otherwise, and you choose to seek new representation. Try to part on good terms and leave the door open. The acting profession is swift-moving and you'll run into the same people time and time again, so it makes good sense to try to keep people on your good side and maintain amicable relations.

The relationship between an agent and their actors is a two-way street. The agent's reputation depends not just on their negotiating skills and rapport with casting directors, but also their clients. You are representing them and so should be professional and avoid behaviour and situations that may reflect badly on the agent.

Simon & How Associates offer their insight into the actor/agent relationship:

"All through history successful people have had trusted advisors whom they can rely upon for sound advice and direction when necessary. Successful actors are no different. Talent needs time to grow and mature and each and every one of those potential rising stars needs sound backup and direction while they hone their craft.

A good agent is not just there to click a button, submit actors for jobs and take commission from their clients. A good talent agent is a person who believes in you, the person they represent, and will carry out on your behalf all the necessary contractual paperwork, negotiating and general day to day workings needed for your success. An agent will take time to search for talent they believe in. They will go to the showcases, and, once they represent you, attend your performances and watch your footage. They will talk to you and get to know your strengths and your weaknesses and will push to get you in front of the right people and seen for the right roles.

Casting directors and producers also rely on agents. In an increasingly saturated and competative industry where a casting director can often receive thousands of submissions for one breakdown, they need trusted agents who will ensure the actor they are suggesting for a role is right for it will go in to a casting and do a great audition.

A good working relationship is built up over the years and mutual trust goes a long way in making the difficult task of castings run smoothly and be less time consuming for all concerned. Without this facilitation the ultimate scenario would be one of mobs of desperate actors pounding on directors and producers doors, trying to fight their way to the front of the line to have their audition heard!

An agent is a must have for all aspiring actors. An agent is a necessary intermediary for bringing the right people together. An agent is a person who believes in you. Think about it, every successful writer, artist, and performer is represented by an agent... it if works for them it must be beneficial."

Personal managers

Some agents are members of the Personal Managers' Association (PMA), offering a wider range of services to their clients – but remember that personal managers are not necessarily the same as agents. Personal managers will work with an actor one-to-one to field contact with the press, arrange tours and so on, as in the music industry, but may not have the same relationship with possible sources of work as an agent does.

The PMA (**www.thepma.com**) has a code of conduct which member agencies adhere to, making the responsibilities of each party clear. The most important part of your relationship with any agent is to stay in touch (without making a nuisance of yourself) – communication will usually clear things up. If you're a member of Equity, you can download the organisation's helpful 'You and Your Agent' booklet from the members' section of the website www.equity.org.uk.

Self-marketing

Your agent is a vital part of your ongoing efforts to get work. This doesn't mean you should cease marketing yourself: keep sending out letters, networking and checking websites and publications for castings. It's to your advantage to market yourself as best you can and to keep plugging away. The agent isn't your sole route to work, so don't be tempted to sign up and assume you can relax and let them do all the work. Agents are likely to respond well to proactive clients, as long as you don't try to interfere with their way of doing things. And it's vital that you check with them to establish a clear working relationship. Some will take commission on all acting earnings, irrespective of whether the work came through them, others will only take commission on work that they put you forward for. If you do attend auditions that you've sourced privately, or if you are offered work (e.g. on a student film, fringe theatre, corporates, commercials etc.) that has not come via your agent do make sure to let your agent know. The last thing they'll want is to be putting you forward only to find out that you're unavailable due to commitments about which they knew nothing.

A-Z of agents

21ST CENTURY ACTORS MANAGEMENT
206 PANTHER HOUSE
38 MOUNT PLEASANT
LONDON WC1X 0AN
020 7278 3438
MAIL@21STCENTURYACTORS.CO.UK
WWW.21STCENTURYACTORS.CO.UK
A Co-operative Management Agency,
based in central London, with strong
theatre and commercial links

A & J MANAGEMENT
242A THE RIDGEWAY
ENFIELD EN2 8AP
020 8367 7139/020 8342 0542
WWW.AJMANAGEMENT.CO.UK
Formed in 1985 by Jackie Michael, A&J
Management is one of the UK's leading
Theatrical Agencies for young people. A&J
has been the embryonic base for many of
the UK's best young actors. These include:
Ben Whishaw, Michelle Ryan, Joe Absolom
and Olivia Hallinan. In line with company
expansion and the inexhaustible demand
for young British talent, A&J now has an
American affiliate, Innovative Artists, a
leading agency with offices in New York
and Los Angeles. While the search for
talent inevitably remains the agency's
principal objective, A&J will continue to be
discerning in selecting fresh and exciting
talent and introducing a galaxy of new
names and new faces.

AAPW ARTISTES
SEAFORD
SUSSEX BN25 4LL
AAPWAGENCY@YAHOO.CO.UK
Representing Actors in Theatre, Musical
Theatre, Opera, Film and TV in addition to
creatives such as Writers and Composers.

ACCESS ARTISTE MANAGEMENT LTD
11-15 BETTERTON STREET
COVENT GARDEN
LONDON WC2H 9BP
020 7866 5444
MAIL@ACCESS-UK.COM
WWW.ACCESS-UK.COM/
We recently celebrated our 10th
anniversary and Access continues to be
considered one of the top agents and
personal managements in London. We
represent artistes in all sectors of the
industry including Actors, Dancers,
Singers, Actor-Musicians, Models,
Musicians, Musical Directors, Directors,
Composers, Playwrights, Presenters &
Voice Over Artistes.

ACCESS ARTISTE MANAGEMENT LTD
11-15 BETTERTON STREET
LONDON WC2H 9BP
020 7866 5444
WWW.ACCESS-UK.COM/
Access was formed in 1999 and grew
quickly into a strong agency and personal

management. Started by people who really understand the performers side of the business, Access set out to change the "Old School" system that the industry is so famous for. Our business is run by young, energetic and vibrant entrepreneurs, striving for the highest success for all our clients, whilst maintaining good, honest, no-nonsense contact with casting companies and producers.

ACTING ASSOCIATES
71 HARTHAM ROAD
LONDON N7 9JJ
020 76073562
FIONA@ACTIBGASSOCIATES.CO.UK
WWW.ACTINGASSOCIATES.CO.UK

ACTORS WORLD CASTING
020 8898 2579
KATHERINE@ACTORS-WORLD-PRODUCTION.COM
WWW.ACTORS-WORLD-PRODUCTION.COM
Actors World Casting provides actors for all occasions. Theatre, film, commercials, corporate work.

ACT'Z
BANK HOUSE, HIGH STREET
STAITHES
SALTBURN-BY-THE-SEA TS13 5BH
01947 891024
ACTZ1@ROCKETMAIL.COM
WWW.ACTZ1.WEBS.COM
Although based in North Yorkshire we represent talented people from across the country. We concentrate on new, young, exciting talent but also have a number of outstanding more mature clients too. Professionalism, whilst combined with a genuine caring attitude towards all of our clients is leading to great success for everyone involved. ACT'Z expects every member to be part of a team where we all work together to be the very best in the business. If you feel you could genuinely fit this bill then please contact us as we'd love to hear from you.

ALEXANDER PERSONAL MANAGEMENT
MAIN ADMINISTRATION BUILDING
RATION BUILDING PINEWOOD STUDIOS IVER HEATH
BUCKS SL0 0NH
017 5363 9204
APM@APMASSOCIATES.NET
WWW.APMASSOCIATES.NET
Linda French & APM Associates (Alexander Personal Management Ltd) was founded in November 1989. Possessing excellent contacts within Film, Television and the West End organisations the agency is one of the stars of the business and through this has a solid reputation for exceptional talent and first-class service. A.P.M. has successfully recruited and marketed clients to major players in the industry: including Working Title, Warner Brothers, Ridley Scott Productions, Eastern Promises Films, La Plante Productions, Disney Corporation, Shed Productions, BBC, Granada, Talkback Thames, Cameron Mackintosh, Really Useful Group, Bill Kenwright, National Theatre, Royal Shakespeare Company and major commercial and corporate producers.

AMANDA HOWARD ASSOCIATES LTD
21 BERWICK STREET
LONDON W1F 0PZ
020 7287 9277
MAIL@AMANDAHOWARDASSOCIATES.CO.UK
WWW.AMANDAHOWARDASSOCIATES.CO.UK
If you wish to submit material for our consideration, please send a cv, photo, explanatory letter and return postage to the address below. Please mark the envelope 'Acting Department'. Please do not send multiple letters to different agents. Please note we only represent professional artists over the age of 16 who live in the UK and Ireland.

AMBER PERSONAL MANAGEMENT
28 ST MARGARET'S CHAMBERS 5 NEWTON STREET
MANCHESTER M1 1HL
016 1228 0236
WWW.AMBERLTD.CO.UK
We are a Film, Television and Theatrical Agency representing a diverse range of actors within all areas of the industry. We specialise in developing each client's individual portfolio, encouraging excellence across the full range of media, particularly television, theatre, radio and film.

ANDERSON SAUNDERS ASSOCIATES
4 GELDESTON ROAD
LONDON E5 8RQ
020 8806 6361
BEL@ANDERSONSAUNDERSASSOCIATES.COM
WWW.ANDERSONSAUNDERSASSOCIATES.COM

We are a newly established theatrical agency based in Hackney, London. We intend to maintain a small client base to ensure personal attention and mentoring. We are prepared to work extraordinarily hard for actors who convince us that nothing will stop them from achieving their goals.

ANDREW MANSON PERSONAL MANAGEMENT
288 MUNSTER ROAD
LONDON SW6 6BQ
020 7386 9158
POST@ANDREWMANSON.COM
WWW.ANDREWMANSON.COM
We are members of the Personal Managers Association and Supporters of British Equity, SAG and AFTRA.

APM ASSOCIATES
PINEWOOD STUDIOS
IVER HEATH
BUCKS. SL0 0NH
01753 639204
APM@APMASSOCIATES.NET
WWW.APMASSOCIATES.NET
Casting and Personal Management. Recent tv credits include Eastenders, Doctor Who, Holby City. Theatre, Oliver, Dinner Ladies, The Harder They Come. Cinema, The Ghost Writer, Harry Potter. Commercials, Pimms, Tesco, Argos

ARENA PERSONAL MANAGEMENT
PANTHER HOUSE
38 MOUNT PLEASANT
LONDON WC1X 0AP
020 7278 1661
ARENAPMLTD@AOL.COM
WWW.ARENAPMLTD.CO.UK
Arena Personal Management is an actor's co-operative agency established in 1985. We represent London based professional actors and secure our clients work in theatre, film, television and radio. We do not represent children, models, or supporting artists.

ASTON MANAGEMENT
ASTON FARM HOUSE
REMENHAM LANE
RG9 3DE
ASTONAGENT@YAHOO.CO.UK
WWW.ASTONMANAGEMENT.ORG
Aston Management is a small agency representing up and coming talent. Currently working with a variety of age groups to create a career path. Aston Mgt also offer local actors casting workshops, LAMDA courses and audition technique workshops.

AXM
308 PANTHER HOUSE
LONDON WC1X 0AN
020 7873 3304
INFO@AXMGT.COM
WWW.AXMGT.COM
We are a Co-operative Agency - one of the best in the business. We are the only Co-operative Agency that is a member of the PMA. In commercial terms we are a small agency with an average of 25 clients on our books. We are always on the look out for talented actors to join us, whether you are fresh from drama school or have been in the business for years. The relatively small nature of our client list means there is a wealth of potential work available to the actors we represent. Recent television work for clients includes Churchill At War (BBC/HBO), Filth: The Mary Whitehouse Story (BBC), Victoria's Men (Channel 4), Sense & Sensibility (BBC), Fallen Angel (ITV), M. I. High (BBC), Annually Retentive (BBC), as well as numerous low budget features and short films. Our recent theatre work includes productions for RSC, Royal Lyceum Edinburgh, Bath Theatre Royal, Bristol Old Vic, Company of Angels, Frantic Assembly, Hackney Empire, London Bubble, National Theatre of Scotland, Nuffield Southampton, Punchdrunk, Royal & Derngate, Stephen Joseph Theatre, Theatre By The Lake, Torch Milford Haven, The Unicorn, Winchester Theatre Royal and No 1 Tours. We are also aware of the need for actors to subsidise their income through commercial, corporate & educational work and we have a strong track record of finding such work for our clients. Our offices are on Mount Pleasant near Chancery Lane and office hours are 10.00 till 18.00, Monday to Friday.

B P A
174 CLARENCE ROAD
FLEET, HAMPSHIRE GU51 3XR
0845 226 0809
AGENT@BOOSTPA.CO.UK
WWW.BOOSTPA.CO.UK/AGENCY
B P A was established in 2006. Whilst the
agency started working initially with
children it has since grown and now has a
client list of children, new graduates and
mature actors. Specialising in Musical
Theatre, and staffed by agents who have
worked extensively in this field and across
the industry, we are proud of our
commitment to developing the careers of
our clients, not merely finding them jobs!

BAM ASSOCIATES
BENETS COTTAGE
DOLBERROW
CHURCHILL BS25 5NT
01934 852 942
CASTING@EBAM.TV
BAM Supplies trained professional
actor's for work throughout the UK and
overseas. We represent artists with a
wide range of experience in Theatre,
Film, Television and Radio, as well as
Corporate and Commercial.

BEAUS AND BELLES
175 MOOR LANE
CHESSINGTON
SURREY KT9 2AB
08444 142 908
INFO@BEAUSANDBELLES.COM
WWW.BEAUSANDBELLES.COM

Beaus and Belles aims to represent new
and diverse talent. You will never find 2
actors the same on our books!

BILLBOARD PERSONAL MANAGEMENT
11 MOWLL STREET
LONDON SW9 6BG
020 7735 9956
INFO@BILLBOARDPM.COM
WWW.BILLBOARDPM.COM
Billboard Personal Management is a
boutique talent agency with over 20
years experience representing highly
skilled actors and actresses across
television, film and theatre. Over that
time we've built an enviable reputation
for offering our clients a level of
personal service, attention, guidance and
support unmatched elsewhere.

BILLY MARSH ASSOCIATES
76A GROVE END ROAD
ST JOHN'S WOOD
LONDON NW8 9ND
020 7449 6930
TALENT@BILLYMARSH.CO.UK
WWW.BILLYMARSH.CO.UK
Billy Marsh associates is one of the most
highly respected names in the entertainment industry. As top television agents
with a unique balance of clients, the
company handles the flourishing careers
of the nations most talented young
artists, as well as being famous for representing a most prestigious and select
list of the longest established names in
T.V, musical theatre and the media.

BLACKBURN SACHS ASSOCIATES

2-4 NOEL STREET
LONDON W1F 8GB
020 7292 7555
PRESENTERS@BLACKBURNSACHSASSOCIATES.COM
WWW.BLACKBURNSACHASSOCIATES.COM
Blackburn Sachs Associates specialise in the creative management of personalities for television, radio and live events.

BLOOMFIELDS MANAGEMENT

77 OXFORD STREET
LONDON
W1D 2ES
020 7659 2001
BARNABY@BLOOMFIELDSMANAGEMENT.COM
Bloomfields Management represents actors in Television, Theatre, Film and Commercials. For further information on the agency go to www.bloomfieldsmanagement.com   POSTAL SUBMISSIONS ONLY PLEASE - NO MESSAGES THROUGH CASTINGCALL PRO

BRONIA BUCHANAN ASSOCIATES LTD

FIRST FLOOR
TAVISTOCK STREET
LONDON WC2E 7NX
020 7395 1400
INFO@BUCHANAN-ASSOCIATES.CO.UK
WWW.BUCHANAN-ASSOCIATES.CO.UK
Buchanan Associates specialises in the personal representation of actors and creatives within the theatre, television and film industry. We pride ourselves on developing and nurturing a diverse and dynamic list of clients and look forward to continuing the tradition of paving exciting careers. Buchanan Associates has an outstanding reputation for looking after calibre actors, musical theatre performers and creatives. Since its inception in 2001, Buchanan Associates has gone from strength to strength in securing clients roles in the most exciting, prolific and successful productions. Our clients are currently employed in Television, Commercials, Film, Musicals, West End, and UK Regional & European Theatre. The agency has an affiliated commercial dance division.

BROOD

HIGH STREET BUILDINGS
134 KIRKDALE
LONDON SE26 4BB
020 8699 1757
BROODMANAGEMENT@AOL.COM
WWW.BROODMANAGEMENT.COM
Established small agency, friendly and relaxed, with a varied client base. Representing all types of actor, from Classical Theatre to Musical Theatre. Unpaid Fringe to High Budget Film/TV. Also represents Models who can act. Most clients in the younger age range. Brood prides itself on good relationships right across the Industry, and all clients are given personal attention as a priority. New applications by email are always welcome, and Brood takes on a small number of new clients each year.

BROWN & SIMCOCKS

1 BRIDGEHOUSE COURT

109 Blackfriars Road
London SE1 8HW
020 7928 1229
MAIL@BROWNANDSIMCOCKS.CO.UK
WWW.BROWNANDSIMCOCKS.CO.UK
Founded in 1978 by Barry Brown, Brown & Simcocks has been representing and nurturing Actors for over thirty years. Many of the clients have been with the company since the beginning. Having joined Barry in 1985, Carrie Simcocks now owns and runs the agency. Kelly Andrews works alongside Carrie and they are ably assisted, as required, by Joyce Rae. Sally Moore has been keeping the books for twenty years, recently joined by Malcolm Ashton.

Burnett Granger Crowther Ltd

3 Clifford Street
London
W1S 2LF
020 7437 8008
ASSOCIATES@BGCLTD.ORG
Theatrical Agents based in the West End of London.

Caravanserai Associates

334B Ladbroke Grove
London
W10 5AS
0560 1534892
INFO@CSERAI.CO.UK
Caravanserai Associates is a dynamic London based acting agency, offering comprehensive and specialised client representation. We work in conjunction with an successful Acting Studio providing our clients with a wealth of available expertise and experience. This gives our clients a unique advantage when preparing for auditions.

CBL Management

20 Hollingbury Rise
Brighton
BN1 7HJ
01273 321245
ENQUIRIES@CBLMANAGEMENT.CO.UK
WWW.CBLMANAGEMENT.CO.UK
CBL Management is a Personal Management service for Artistes, Creative and Production personnel established in response to the growing demands for excellence within the entertainment industry.   Boasting a carefully selected client list our stress is on the personal; dedicating our time and efforts to understanding and developing our artistes' skills and strengths in order to secure suitable castings and contracts.

Celex Casting

Celex Casting Ltd
PO BOX 7317
Derby DE1 0GS
01332 232445
ANNE@CELEX.CO.UK
Celex Casting represents a large client base in the midlands. Representing both Actors and Supporting Artists we also have a comprehensive data base of pre-licensed children. We are a BBC approved agency working on

programmes such as Doctors, Casualty, Dr Who, Survivors to name a few. Also Shameless, and Hustle.

CHRIS DAVIS MANAGEMENT LTD

ST MARTIN'S HOUSE
59 ST MARTIN'S LANE
LONDON WC2N 4JS
020 7240 2116
INFO@CDM-LTD.COM
WWW.CDM-LTD.COM

Chris Davis Management is a leading personal management agency offering a highly professional level of artiste representation. The company has a diverse client base, which leads us to be active in all areas of the entertainment industry both in the UK and internationally. Our client list includes actors, personalities, singers, directors, choreographers, musical directors and lighting designers, working in film, television, theatre, and concerts. The experienced and dedicated team is headed by director Chris Davis, who founded the agency 15 years ago. The company has offices in London and the Midlands.

CHRIS SNODE SPORTS PROMOTIONS

56 CHURCH ROAD
CRYSTAL PALACE
LONDON SE19 2EZ
020 8771 4700
AGENT@SPORTSPROMOTIONS.CO.UK
WWW.SPORTSPROMOTIONS.CO.UK

We were originally a Sports Agency - established in 1990 by Chris Snode, Olympian competitor, world Diving Champion and TV Commentator. We provide and exclusive sports service to advertising agencies, production companies, photographers and TV companies. We are based at Crystal Palace and can organise facilities, castings, sports locations, models and equipment hire. The reason we have so many people on the books at present is because we try and cover ever sport you can possible think of. For example, Football, Rugby, Cricket, Circus Skills, Gymnastic, Dancers, free runners, basket ball, Martial arts, Body Builders, kite surfers and fit all rounder's (and there are more). We have many actors on our books who have worked in TV and films like Little Britain, Harry Potter, Bourne ultimatum,Batman, Stardust and Your Highness movie. The acting side of the agency is expanding.

CHRISTOPHER ANTHONY ASSOCIATES

THE OLD DAIRY 164 THAMES ROAD
LONDON W4 3QS
020 8994 9952
WWW.CHRISTOPHERANTHONY.CO.UK

CINEL GABRAN MANAGEMENT

PO BOX 5163
CANTON
CARDIFF CF5 9BJ
02920 666600
WWW.CINELGABRAN.CO.UK

Cinel Gabran Management is a Personal

Management Company for Actors, Presenters and Directors. The company was originally founded in Glasgow in 1988 and after a period of trading from Hertfordshire, moved its main office to Cardiff in 2000. The Company now has offices in Cardiff and North Yorkshire and maintains a National Client List. The Company represents Actors for both English and Welsh Language Productions and Voice-over work.

CIRCUIT PERSONAL MANAGEMENT LTD
SUITE 71, SEC
BEDFORD STREET
STOKE ON TRENT ST1 4PZ
01782 285388
MAIL@CIRCUITPM.CO.UK
WWW.CIRCUITPM.CO.UK
Trained and experienced actors for stage, tv, radio, film, corporate, role play, voice over.

CLAYPOLE MANAGEMENT
PO BOX 123
DARLINGTON
DL3 7WA
0845 650 1777
CLAYPOLE_1@HOTMAIL.COM
WWW.CLAYPOLEMANAGEMENT.CO.UK
Claypole Management have been providing the entertainment industry with performers and artistes for nearly a decade. We represent artistes from all over the UK, with bases in London and the North East. We have built a reputation for quality and excellence by consistently providing high quality professional actors for film/television/theatre & media advertising.

CLIC AGENCY
RHOSLWYN
RHOS ISAF
GWYNEDD LL54 7NF
01286 831001
CLIC@BTINTERNET.COM
Clic Agency is based in North Wales but represents artistes nationally. Web site clicagency.co.uk

CLIVE CORNER ASSOCIATES
THE BELENES
60 WAKEHAM
PORTLAND DT5 1HN
01305 860267
CORNERASSOCIATES@AOL.COM
Clive Corner Associates was small but perfectly formed in 1987. Now handles a select list of experienced clients and rarely takes newcomers.

CLOUD NINE AGENCY
96 TIBER GARDENS
TREATY STREET
LONDON N1 0XE
020 7278 0029
INFO@CLOUDNINEAGENCY.CO.UK
WWW.CLOUDNINEAGENCY.CO.UK
Cloud Nine Agency is primarily based in North London. The agency was founded in 1995 Since 1995 the company has grown through it's own merit and determination

to succeed. Cloud Nine Agency aims to offer a high quality service with a friendly and personal touch that we feel is so important within this industry. Cloud Nine Agency can provide a service across a wide spectrum within the industry; by this we mean to Artistes, Casting Directors and also Advertising / Production Companies. We particularly specialize in Television, Commercials, Theatre and Musical Theatre also Corporate / Music Videos Cloud Nine Agency actively encourages artistes to continue seeking work through their own contacts and therefore we do not take a percentage fee for work which our artistes find independently. To demonstrate our commitment to service we keep our artistes informed of all their submissions in a regular individual newsletter.

CONWAY CAN GELDER LTD
8/12 BROADWICK STREET
LONDON W1F 8HW
020 7287 1070
WWW.CONWAYVANGELDER.COM

CRESCENT MANAGEMENT
10 BARLEY MOW PASSAGE
LONDON
W4 4PH
020 8987 0191
MAIL@CRESCENTMANAGEMENT.CO.UK
If you are an actor and would like to be considered for membership of Crescent Management you must send us a HARD COPY (i.e. by post) of your CV, a

photograph and a cover note indicating why you wish to be part of a Co-Operative Management. Please note that your application will not be considered unless you are a member of Equity and†have an entry in The Spotlight. Crescent Management will need to see your work, either on stage or screen,†before your application can be taken further.

DARREN GRAY MANAGEMENT
2 MARSTON LANE
PORTSMOUTH
HAMPSHIRE PO3 5TW
023 92699973
DARREN.GRAY1@VIRGIN.NET
www.darrengraymanagement.co.uk
Darren Gray Management represents Australian actors, producers, directors and writers whilst they are working in the UK.

DAVID DALY ASSOCIATES
586 KING'S ROAD
LONDON SW6 2DX
020 7384 1036
AGENT@DAVIDDALY.CO.UK
WWW.DAVIDDALY.CO.UK
David Daly Associates is an established actors agency bringing 30 years of experience to the entertainment industry. David is joined in the London office by Louisa Clifton, assisted by Ivy Henry and in the Northern office by Mary Ramsay, assisted by Rosalind Bach to provide a distinctive personal service to all our clients.

DEALERS AGENCY BELFAST
CATHEDRAL HOUSE
23-31 WARING STREET
BELFAST BT1 2DX
028 9020 9761
INFO@DEALERSAGENCY.CO.UK
WWW.DEALERSAGENCY.CO.UK

Dealers Agency represents the cream of Northern Irish Talent, as we continue to provide the industry here with actors for our televisions, films and for the stage.

DENMARK STREET MANAGEMENT
SUITE 4 CLARENDON BUILDINGS
25 HORSELL ROAD
LONDON N5 1XL
020 7700 5200
MAIL@DENMARKSTREET.NET
WWW.DENMARKSTREET.NET

Established in 1985, Denmark Street Management has developed over the years to become one of the UK's leading co-operative agencies - specialising in providing highly skilled professional actors for theatre, film, television, commercials and radio.   For details on how to apply to the agency, please visit www.denmarkstreet.net/apply.html

DP MANAGEMENT
ARGYLE HOUSE
29-31 EUSTON ROAD
LONDON NW1 2SD
DANNY@DPMANAGEMENT.ORG

DP Management represents Actors, Dancers and Singers

dQ MANAGEMENT
27 RAVENSWOOD PARK
NORHTWOOD
MIDDLESEX HA6 3PR
012 7372 1221
DQ.MANAGEMENT1@GOOGLEMAIL.COM
WWW.DQMANAGEMENT.COM

dQ management was established in 2003 by Kate Davis (a hugely unsuccessful actress in her own right) who was keen to bridge the gap between artist and agent, forming working partnerships whereby each actor could still feel they had control over their own career whilst remaining confident in the hard-working and supportive team behind them. The reputation of dQ has built up purely on the strength of the artists we choose to represent. Subsequently, dQ are a very selective agency that looks for not only the strongest talent, but passion, commitment, professionalism and an all-round nice person. Our aim is to remain small and personal to maintain strong relationships between each individual actor. Our clients work in Film, TV, Theatre, Musical Theatre and Commercials.

DRAGON PERSONAL MANAGEMENT

96 DIANA STREET
ROATH
CARDIFF CF24 4TU
02920 193974
CASTING@DRAGON-PM.COM
WWW.DRAGON-PM.COM

Dragon Personal Management provides diverse range of experienced actors to the industry. Dragon is run by industry professionals and an experienced entrepreneur with a masters in Business. We pride ourselves on providing both the artists we represent and casting directors with a first class service. Please contact us for details at any time.

ELINOR HILTON ASSOCIATES

1 GOODWINS COURT
LONDON WC2N 4LL
020 7240 2555
INFO@ELINORHILTON.COM
WWW.ELINORHILTON.COM

Based in Central London, Elinor Hilton Associates represents actors and directors across all branches of the industry.

ELITE-TALENT LTD

54 CROSSLEE RD
BLACKLEY
MANCHESTER M9 6TA
JACKIE@ELITE-TALENT.COM
WWW.ELITE-TALENT.COM

Elite is a management agency with offices in London and Greater Manchester. We operate a small client list of professional actors. We pride ourselves on searching for new talent and focusing our energies in providing opportunities for our actors. Our artistes work in all aspects of the industry; television, theatre, commercials, film and radio.

ELSPETH COCHRANE PERSONAL MANAGEMENT

16 TRINITY CLOSE
THE PAVEMENT
LONDON SW4 0JD
020 7622 3566
WWW.ELSPETHCOCHRANE.COM

Elspeth Cochrane Personal Management is one of the oldest theatrical agencies, having been established in 1960. Founded by Elspeth Cochrane, who had herself trained at the Webber Douglas School of Drama and Music before working extensively as an actress. Miss Cochrane has always believed in bringing people of all talents together and being the midwife to the birth of a new project. Since its foundation many of the most distinguished artists in these disciplines have been on her books and her knowledge and experience is second to none. Today, as before her clients include as ever-talented writers, directors, designers and actors. Today, ECPM is joined by Tony Barlow who has also had wide experience in the theatre as Administrator as well as in Press and Marketing.

ETV MEDIA GROUP
8 PARK PLACE, LAWN LANE
VAUXHALL
SW8 1UD
020 7820 4470
JUSTINE.COLLINS@ETV.TV
WWW.ETV.TV
ETV media group is a television
company specialising in digital and
branded content

EVOLUTION TALENT AGENCY
THE TRUMAN BUILDING
91 BRICK LANE
LONDON E1 6QL
020 7770 6128
LOFTY@EVOLUTIONMNGT.COM
WWW.EVOLUTIONMNGT.COM
Evolution is focused on nurturing the
artistic growth, professionalism and
individual fulfilment of those under its
care, working together with the artist in
developing their long-term career
achievements.   ABOUT US   Evolution
was founded in 1999 as part of the
Agency Group based at Belgrave Square
in London. In 2000 it branched out on
its own, moved to the Truman Building
and has steadily been growing over the
past 5 years.   The talent division covers
stage, film, television, radio and also
commercial work.

FABNEWFACES
PO BOX 62746
LONDON SW2 9FZ
020 8674 6174
INFO@FABNEWFACES.CO.UK
WWW.FABNEWFACES.CO.UK
FABNEWFACES is a great and reliable
agency. We support new faces, as well
as established Models and Actors -
babies to the maturer adult. We always
try and supply what the client is looking
for, in a helpful and easy manner.
FABNEWFACES is a great helpful agency,
with years of experience behind us.

GALLOWAYS ONE
15 LEXHAM MEWS
LONDON W8 6JW
020 7376 2288
EMAIL@GALLOWAYSONE.COM
WWW.GALLOWAYSONE.COM
We have been one of the leading agents
in London for over 25 years, representing actors principally for featured
commercials but also for training films,
corporate films and presentations for
both the UK and abroad. We also have
close ties with JGM who represent
actors for television, film and theatre.
Our clients' cover a broad spectrum of
ages and looks, to enable us to help
with most casting briefs. We have a
strict interview policy, which guarantees
that we only represent quality actors of
an excellent professional standard and
reliability and we are constantly interviewing prospective new clients to

maintain high standards. We already work with all the top advertising agencies, production companies and television companies in the UK and Europe and we look forward to working with you.

GARDNER HERRITY
24 CONWAY STREET
LONDON W1T 6BG
020 7388 0088
INFO@GARDNERHERRITY.CO.UK
WWW.GARDNERHERRITY.CO.UK

GAVIN RYDER ASSOCIATES
NORTHERN QUATRE
MANCHESTER M60 7RA
0161 408 5616
GAVINDRYDER@GMAIL.COM
gavinryderassociates.co.nr
Gavin Ryder Associates is a small boutique Agency representing Actors in Film, TV and Theatre. We provide a comprehensive, specialised and highly individual service for our clients.

GFM ASSOCIATES
20 ALLENFORD HOUSE
TUNWORTH CRESCENT
LONDON SW15 4PG
020 8878 3105
GFMASSOCIATES@LIVE.CO.UK
Small, selective London based agency providing representation and personal management for actors in film, television, commercials and theatre. We pride ourselves on representing and

promoting a carefully selected portfolio of dedicated, highly-skilled actors of a very high calibre with a genuine love of their craft. Some emphasis on actors with international appeal, fluency in a second or third language and exceptional screen-acting ability.

GILBERT & PAYNE PERSONAL MANAGEMENT
ROOM 236, 2ND FLOOR, LINDEN HALL
162-168 REGENT STREET
LONDON W1B 5TB
020 7734 7505
EE@GILBERTANDPAYNE.COM
WWW.GILBERTANDPAYNE.COM
Gilbert and Payne is a leading Personal Management Company, representing Actors and Creatives working worldwide in the entertainment industry. We specialise in providing artists and creatives for theatre, film and television
.

GLOBAL ARTISTS
23 HAYMARKET
LONDON SW1Y 4DG
020 7839 4888
INFO@GLOBALARTISTS.CO.UK
WWW.GLOBALARTISTS.CO.UK
Global Artists is a leading personal management company for professional Actors and Creatives working worldwide in the Entertainment Industry. From one of the busiest media and theatre capitals of the world, Global Artists is located in the United Kingdom in the heart of London's West End. With

over 90 years of combined experience, Global Artists offers a unique, professional and personal management for Actors and Creatives working in Theatre, Musical Theatre, Film and Television.

GRANTHAM-HAZELDINE

SUITE 315, THE LINEN HALL
162-168 REGENT STREET
LONDON W1B 5TD
020 7038 3737/3738
AGENTS@GRATHAMHAZELDINE.COM
WWW.GRANTHAMHAZELDINE.COM

John Grantham started the agency in 1985 following a successful career as an actor. In 1996 he was joined by Caroline Hazeldine, who returned from nine years working in the Industry in Los Angeles to form the partnership that is Grantham-Hazeldine. In April 2007 they were joined by Alastair Lindsey–Renton, as an associate working on a full time basis. Alastair brings with him a great deal of experience in both teaching and performing and substantial connections in the world of musical theatre and film. Having all started out as actors we are always 100% committed to our clients long term careers not just 'the next job'. With 20 years of experience in the industry we have excellent working relationships with most of the successful casting directors. We keep our client base small (around 85 men and women) so that we are able to work with and for our clients individually. Unlike many other agents we require all our clients to phone in at least once a week. We are always available to clients and casting directors and clients will always deal directly with one of us, never with an assistant.

GRAYS MANAGEMENT LTD

PANTHER HOUSE
38 MOUNT PLEASANT
LONDON WC1X 0AP
020 7278 1054
GRAYS.MAN@BTCONNECT.COM
WWW.GRAYSMAN.COM

Grays Management is a well-established theatrical agency representing Actors for TV, Film, Theatre and Corporate work, with an extensive knowledge of the industry and vast experience. Grays has a firm and passionate belief in talent and we are dedicated to improving the standard of actors in employment.

HALL JAMES PERSONAL MANAGEMENT

PO BOX 604
PINNER
MIDDLESEX HA5 9GH
020 8429 8111
INFO@HALLJAMES.CO.UK
WWW.HALLJAMES.CO.UK

Hall James Personal Management was established in 2006, by Sam Hall and Stori James, and represents a wide variety of Artists of exceptional talent within Theatre and Television. Coming from successful creative and performing backgrounds ourselves, we have a genuine passion and energy for the business. We aim to meet the requirements of today's industry by supplying top class professionals, whilst providing our clients with individual care and attention at all times.

HAMILTON HODELL LTD
66-68 MARGARET STREET
LONDON W1W 8SR
020 7636 1221
WWW.HAMILTONHODELL.CO.UK

HAT MANAGEMENT
24, THORNLEY RISE
AUDENSHAW
MANCHESTER M34 5JX
0161 3708648
HAT.MGMT@HOTMAIL.CO.UK
Actor's Agent. Concentrating on Televison and Theatre work for professional actor's.

HENRY'S AGENCY
53 WESTBURY
ROCHFORD
ESSEX SS4 IUL
017 0254 1413
CASTING@HENRYSAGENCY.CO.UK
WWW.HENRYSAGENCY.CO.UK

HOBSON'S ACTORS
62 CHISWICK HIGH ROAD
LONDON W4 1SY
020 8995 3628
ACTORS@HOBSONS-INTERNATIONAL.COM
WWW.HOBSONS-INTERNATIONAL.COM
Hobsons is an artists agency with a recording studio based in Chiswick, West London. It was established in 1986 by Sue Bonnici as a voice-over agency, indeed the company name was inspired by the cockney rhyming slang for Voice - Hobson's Choice. Today, we represent over 600 artists with collective experience in all aspects of the media business. We are very much a people business, with a reputation built on a friendly, flexible and knowledgeable service, so please don't hesitate to call us for any additional help or information.

IMPERIAL PERSONAL MANAGEMENT LTD
102 KIRKSTALL ROAD
LEEDS LS3 1JA
01132 443222
KATIE@IPMCASTING.COM
WWW.IPMCASTING.COM
Since it was founded in 2007, Imperial Personal Management Ltd has established an outstanding reputation for providing experienced Professional actors to the entertainment industry covering mainstream Theatre, Television and Film roles. Run by Industry Professionals: we provide Professional Actor Management for highly skilled credible artists. We currently have some well-known faces, and the majority of our clients have relevant experience.

INDEPENDENT TALENT GROUP LTD
OXFORD HOUSE
76 OXFORD STREET
LONDON W1D 1BS
020 7323 2345/020 7323 0101
INFO@ADVOICE.CO.UK
www.independenttalent.com
Independent is Europe's leading privately owned, full service talent agency, formerly known as ICM. In this context 'talent' encompasses actors and actresses, directors, writers, producers and their production companies, models, casting directors, presenters, below-the-line personnel, voiceover artists and others involved in all aspects of the media business. The agency has an established reputation for being proactive in our approach to the representation of talent in the media industries worldwide. We also have a distinctive and unrivalled understanding of the global entertainment industry today and provide a comprehensive, specialised and highly individual service for our clients.

INFINITE ARTISTS LLP
SUITE 105
PINEWOOD STUDIOS
IVER HEATH SL0 0NH
01753 650733
ENQUIRIES@INFINITE-ARTISTS.CO.UK
WWW.INFINITE-ARTISTS.CO.UK
A newly formed talent management agency by Gareth Owen and Andrew Boyle who have been in the management industry for 8 years.

INNER CITY CASTING
PORTLAND TOWER
PORTLAND STREET
MANCHESTER M1 3LF
01942 321969
WWW.ICCAST.CO.UK
Inter-City Casting began life as one of the first Manchester's actors' co-operatives in 1982. Since then it has evolved to offer personal management, run solely by Caroline Joynt (herself once a member of the co-op). As an agency it strives to complement the family feel of the old co-op but with the business acumen of new management, thereby retaining its position as one of the top northern agencies.

INTERNATIONAL ARTIST LTD
4TH FLOOR, HOLBORN HALL
193-197 HIGH HOLBORN
LONDON WC1V 7BD
020 7025 0600
RECEPTION@INTERNATIONALARTISTES.COM
WWW.INTERNATIONALARTISTES.COM
Established in 1946, International Artistes is widely acknowledged as one of the most successful talent management & agency companies in the UK. The company's diverse client base includes numerous high profile performers and actors, as well as many of the UK's top writers producers and directors in television, film and theatre.

JANET PLATER MANAGEMENT LTD
D FLOOR MILBURN HOUSE
DEAN STREET
NEWCASTLE UPON TYNE NE1 1LF
0191 221 2490
INFO@JANETPLATERMANAGEMENT.CO.UK
WWW.JANETPLATERMANAGEMENT.CO.UK
The leading actors agency in the North
East representing around 65 profes-
sional actors. The company also has
another division JPM EXTRAS for extras,
supporting artists and children.

JANICE TILDSLEY ASSOCIATES
47 ORFORD ROAD
LONDON
E17 9NJ
020 8521 1888
INFO@JANICETILDSLEYASSOCIATES.CO.UK
WWW.JANICETILDSLEYASSOCIATES.CO.UK
Janice Tildsley Associates represent a
strong list of musical performers, from
recent graduates to some of the West
End's most talented singers, dancers and
actors. In addition, the agency is
constantly developing a selective but
diverse list of actors, experienced in
television, theatre, film and
commercials.Please send hard copies of
details with a s.a.e.

JEFFREY &WHITE MANAGEMENT
NO 2 LADYGROVE COURT, HITCHWOOD LANE
PRESTON, HITCHIN
HERTFORDSHIRE SG4 7SA
01462 433752
INFO@JEFFREYANDWHITE.CO.UK
WWW.JEFFREYANDWHITE.CO.UK
Jeffrey & White has been established in
the West End of London for some 22
years and has earned a reputation at the
highest level of personal management
covering all aspects of the media. The
agency is headed by Judith Jeffrey.

JGM TALENT
15 LEXHAM MEWS
LONDON W8 6JW
020 7376 2414
MAIL@JGMTALENT.COM
WWW.JGMTALENT.COM
JGM has been providing actors for
Musical Theatre, Theatre, TV, Film and
Radio for the past 10 years.

JOHN DOE MANAGEMENT
123 BANISTER ROAD
LONDON
NW10 3DN
020 8960 2848
CASTING@JOHNDOEMGT.COM
Welcome to John Doe Management, an
agency established and managed by
professionals with extensive experience
across all sectors of the entertainment
industry, including casting, production,
public relations and media liaison. We
are a dedicated team whose
backgrounds give us a leading edge
when it comes to inside knowledge of
the industry. Here at John Doe we
represent professional, creative and
talented actors by providing each with
individual attention, professionalism and

integrity. Our top priority and primary objective is to provide the industry with quality and professional talent. As well as an established client base involving television, film and commercial work, we also strive to find, and represent fresh talent and help them to develop their career aspirations and goals.   Our diverse assortment of talent have all been hand picked for their unique skills and characteristics. We not only provide actor's who closely fit the casting brief but determined, focused performers who meet our high standards of profession-alism and reliability and help to create a good rapport between Client, Agent and Casting Director.

JOHNSTON AND MATHERS ASSOCIATES
PO BOX 3167
BARNET
LONDON EN5 2WA
020 8449 4968
WWW.JOHNSTONMATHERS.COM
Being a relatively small agency, we like to work closely with our clients- as a team. The success of the people we represent is also our success, hence we share a common aim.

JONATHAN ARUN LIMITED COMMERCIALS
33 STANNARY STREET
LONDON SE11 4AA
020 7840 0123
JEFF@JONATHANARUN.COM
WWW.JONATHANARUN.COM
Jonathan Arun Limited is a talent agency

that represents and advises artists of outstanding talent and International reputation. The agency's vision is to develop agent-client relationships where every client knows that they and their talent are appreciated - this is the priority.   Founded by Jonathan Arun in 2007, the agency is one of London's boutique talent agencies. Maintaining a small client list with a dedication to personal service and great communica-tion are what Jonathan believes make a difference in the industry. The reputation of Jonathan Arun Limited has been built on these ideals and it is how we work on a daily basis to develop and support our client's careers.   Jonathan Arun Ltd, one of London's boutique styled talent agencies is pleased to announce a new arm of our business dedicated to just Commercials. Jonathan Arun Ltd Commercials will focus on just the advertising aspect of our business and is seeking talent who are interested in maximizing their commercial potential and entering into the lucrative commercial arena.   We are currently actively recruiting faces of all types, shapes, sizes and ages. The commercials industry often asks for actors and actresses of very specific types and skills and we understand it is the wealth of those types and skills that make actors unique and individual. We are seeking talent with vibrant personalities, personal style and their own sense of beauty. If you are interested in meeting to discuss your personal commercial potential and the possibility of joining our Jonathan Arun Limited Commercials, please get in touch at your convenience. You can reach us by sending your headshot and CV to Commercials@JonathanArun.com and we will be in touch to setup a meeting in our London offices. Further information regarding our agency can be found at www.JonathanArun.com .

JULIE FOX ASSOCIATES LTD
NO CONTACT BY POST
EMAIL ONLY
SL6 7NF
01628 777853
AGENT@JULIEFOXASSOCIATES.CO.UK
Having worked as an agent with Tim Kent Associates for 4 years Julie Fox took over the agency in 2009. We have a small client list working in all areas of the industry.

K TALENT
24-25 MACKLIN STREET
COVENT GARDEN
LONDON WC2B 5NN
020 7691 8930
MEL@KTALENT.CO.UK
WWW.KTALENT.CO.UK
K Talent is an Agency representing clients in Musical Theatre, Theatre, TV and Film. There are 4 Agents who work at K Talent and we offer personal Management.

KARUSHI MANAGEMENT LTD
UNIT 10
7 WENLOCK ROAD
LONDON N1 7SL
0845 900 5511
LISA@KARUSHI.COM
WWW.KARUSHI.COM
Karushi Management is a leading talent management agency, renowned for representing a wide variety of artist both new and established working in film, television, radio, theatre stand up comedy and writing.

KATHERINE GREGOR ASSOCIATES
THE COLOMBO CENTRE
34-68 COLOMBO STREET
LONDON SE1 8DP
020 7261 9466
AGENT@KATHERINEGREGORASSOCIATES.CO.UK
WWW.KATHERINEGREGORASSOCIATES.CO.UK
Katherine Gregor Associates officially opened on 1st July 2007, representing actors and directors within the fields of theatre, film, television, radio and commercials.   Our policy is to serve the best interests of our artists, doing everything in our power to further their careers and professional development by offering guidance wherever appropriate, and supporting new ventures. To help achieve this, we find that regular communication and contact is of paramount importance. Consequently, clients are kept informed of all the projects for which their details are submitted, and encouraged to keep in touch by

telephoning the office at least once a month, and coming in personally for a chat at least every three months.

KEDDIE SCOTT ASSOCIATES
STUDIO 1, 17 SHORTS GARDEN
COVENT GARDEN
LONDON WC2H 9AT
020 7836 6802
FIONA@KS-ASS.CO.UK
WWW.KS-ASS.CO.UK
KSA has been established since 2003 and has been growing in leaps and bounds both in reputation and success. We deal in practically every area of the performing industry including TV, Film, Commercials, Theatre, Musical Theatre (Small/Mid/Large Scale) and Corporate Assignments of every nature. Our team is made up of individuals who have all-round professional experience in the business including Performing, Tutoring, Directing, Producing, Stage Managing, Company Managing and Casting. It is the amalgamation of this knowledge that allows us to understand the Industry from every angle. We aim to fully support our artists with profes-sional advice, encouragement and genuine empathy. We employ a fresh new approach to representation whereby we have regular meetings to discuss strategies and plans to assist clients on their path to a successful career in the Industry. Please note that KSA operates on a Personal Exclusive Management basis. For Casting Directors

we provide very selective and careful suggestions. We have an extensive range of talented artistes with various special skills and diverse ranges of experience. We have spent considerable time choosing only the best for our book. The main objective of KSA is to present to you the most suitable artists to be considered as per the criteria of your breakdowns. We embrace modern day technology and will be happy to submit in whichever format suits you best.

KEDDIE SCOTT ASSOCIATES (SCOTTISH OFFICE)
(0/1) 430 TANTALLON ROAD
LANGSIDE
GLASGOW G41 3HR
SCOTLAND@KS-ASS.CO.UK

KELLY MANAGEMENT LTD
11-15 BETTERTON STREET
COVENT GARDEN
LONDON WC2H 9BP
020 7470 8757
OFFICE@KELLY-MANAGEMENT.COM
WWW.KELLY-MANAGEMENT.COM
Kelly Management is a boutique management agency and member of the Personnel Management Association based in Convent Garden, we represent clients in Theatre, Film, Radio and T.V.

KEN MCREDDIE LTD

91 REGENT STREET
LONDON W1R 7TB
020 7439 1456
EMAIL@KENMCREDDIE.COM
WWW.KENMCREDDIE.COM

A leading UK agency representing top British and International Talent with links throughout the world. We represent actors and directors in all areas of the industry. Through Marcus Evans entertainment, we have substantial backing to develop film, television and theatre production.

KENNETH EARLE PERSONAL MANAGEMENT

214 BRIXTON ROAD
LONDON SW9 6AP
020 7274 1219
KENNETHEARLE@AGENTS-UK.COM
WWW.ENTERTAINMENT-KENNETHEARLE.CO.UK

Kenneth Earle Personal Management has a high profile client list incorporating Actors, Actresses, Authors, Directors, Light Entertainment, etc.

KEW PERSONAL MANAGEMENT

PO Box 679
RH1 9BT
020 8871 3697
INFO@KEWPERSONALMANAGEMENT.COM
WWW.KEWPERSONALMANAGEMENT.COM

KEW Personal Management represents male and female adults of all ages in all aspects of the arts. Applications preferred by email.

LIME ACTOR'S AGENCY & MANAGEMENT

NEMESIS HOUSE, 1 OXFORD COURT
BISHOPSGATE
MANCHESTER M2 3WQ
0161 2360827
GEORGINA@LIMEMANAGEMENT.CO.UK
WWW.LIMEMANAGEMENT.TV

Lime Actors Agency & Management was established in 1997 and has since secured an enviable reputation as one of the leading acting agencies in the North of England, supplying professional actors for work in all aspects of the Entertainment Industry including Theatre, Television, Film, Radio & Commercials World Wide. Our clients range from established named artists through to some of the most exciting new talent in the industry, culminating in a very select, but versatile, roster of artistes. We provide an intimate style of personal management, catering to the individual and unique needs of every actor and client. We pride ourselves in offering a very efficient and professional service.

LIZ BISSET MANAGEMENT

272 BATH STREET
GLASGOW G2 4JR
0844 800 6662
LEE@LIZBISSETMANAGEMENT.CO.UK
WWW.LIZBISSETMANAGEMENT.CO.UK

Liz Bisset Management is Scotland's longest established model and casting agency. Supplying talented artists from aged 3 to 70 plus, for Film, TV, and

Commercial Work. We currently have over 300 Extras on our books. Please feel free to check our facebook group Liz Bisset Management for regular updates on what is happening within the agency. We also manage appx 50 Actors www.lizbissetmanagement.co.uk

LIZ HOBBS GROUP LTD
65 LONDON ROAD
NEWARK
NOTTINGHAMSHIRE NG24 1RZ
0870 0702 702
WWW.LIZHOBBSGROUP.COM
Liz Hobbs Group Ltd (LHG) is one of the country's leading producers of concerts and events, working with some of the world's greatest venues and clients, including football stadia, motor racing circuits, exquisite gala dinners, international festivals and the UK's top racecourses.

LOUISE GUBBAY ASSOCIATES
26 WESTMORE ROAD
TATSFIELD
KENT TN16 2AX
01959 573080
LOUISE@LOUISEGUBBAY.COM
WWW.LOUISEGUBBAY.COM
At the age of 16, Louise started her career working as an office junior for her father, Mr Raymond Gubbay CBE, who is Europe's most successful Classical Concert Promoter. From then on, she worked with English National Ballet, Kilroy TV and The Lyceum Theatre before returning to Raymond Gubbay Ltd. Throughout her 17 years in Events Management (which often resulted in working with some highly regarded international artistes) Louise's professionalism was getting her noticed by many. After making an extremely hard decision to leave Raymond Gubbay Ltd, it was clear that timing was right for Louise to start up her own business. LGA was established in 2008 and within the first year, Louise's clients were being continually seen by many of the UK's leading West End Casting Directors including David Grindrod, Pippa Ailion, Debbie O'Brien, Trevor Jackson, Anne Vosser and the Donmar as well as other elite names on the TV/Film side. LGA clients are dealt with nothing but the highest level of professionalism. Louise is passionate about what she does and who she represents. She also prides herself on being very approachable and on building strong, positive relationships with all of her clients.

LOVETT LOGAN ASSOCIATES
40 MARGARET STREET
LONDON W1G 0JH
020 7495 6400
INFO@PLA-UK.COM
Established Actors Agency with offices in London and Edinburgh, representing actors in Film, Television, Theatre, Radio and Advertising.

MACFARLANE CHARD ASSOCIATES

33 PERCY STREET
LONDON W1T 2DF
020 7636 7750
ENQUIRES@MACFARLANCE-CHARD.CO.UK
WWW.MACFARLANE-CHARD.CO.UK

MacFarlane Chard Associates was established in 1994, and has gone on to become one of the leading literary and talent agencies in the UK. In 2006, we expanded our operations to Ireland, and in 2007 amalgamated Dublin agency TMG into our operations to create one of Ireland''s largest talent agencies, MacFarlane Chard (Ireland) Limited.

MACFARLANE DOYLE ASSOCIATES

125 HOOLE ROAD
CHESTER
CHESHIRE CH2 3NW
01244 347091
ROSS.MACFARLANE@BTINTERNET.COM
WWW.MACFARLANEDOYLE.COM

Founded in 2009 as personal managers to represent actors in stage and recorded media work by Perry Doyle and Ross MacFarlane. Both have had careers as actors and have considerable experience of working for West End agencies. Based in Chester and London.

MACNAUGHTON LORD REPRESENTATION

DOUGLAS HOUSE, 16-18 DOUGLAS STREET
WESTMINSTER
LONDON SW1P 4PB
020 7834 4646
INFO@MLREP.COM

WWW.MLREP.COM

This Agency was established in 1967 and has subsequently acquired an international reputation, representing writers, directors, composers, lyricists and designers for stage, screen, classical music and television. We have a particular interest in musical theatre and have developed, been associated with and occasionally produced musicals in Britain and the United States.

MANAGEMENT 2000

11, WELL STREET
TREUDDYN
FLINTSHIRE CH7 4NH
01352 771231
JACKEY@MANAGEMENT-2000.CO.UK

MANAGEMENT 2000 represents a broad spectrum of professional actors, covering all ages and types, from recent graduates to a star of the original 'Crossroads'! All our clients have been carefully chosen for their ability, and the majority have had experience in several media types. MANAGEMENT 2000 is situated in North Wales and we represent a number of Welsh speakers. However our clients are based all over Great Britain and whatever the casting needs, we have an actor or actress to meet them.

MARGARET HOWARD AGENCY

HIGH STREET
BUSHEY
HERTS WD23 1TT

020 8421 8008
MHAGENCY@AOL.COM
The Margaret Howard Agency (MHA)is a
newly established theatrical agency with
excellent contacts throughout the entertainment industry in TV / Film /
Commercial / West End. All our agents
have between 5 - 15 years of experience
each and have joined together to create
a new and exciting agency with a vision
and drive.

THE MARKHAM AGENCY

405 STRAND
LONDON
WC2R 0NE
020 7836 4111
INFO@THEMARKHAMAGENCY.COM
WWW.THEMARKHAMAGENCY.COM
The Markham Agency is one of the UK's
leading talent agencies offering a highly
individual personal management style of
representation for actors & directors
working in film, television, theatre, radio
& voice work. The Markham Agency
Ltd is a member of the Personal
Managers' Association.

MARKHAM & FROGGATT LTD

4 WINDMILL STREET
LONDON W1T 2HZ
020 7636 4412
ADMIN@MARKHAMFROGGATTIRWIN.COM
WWW.MARKHAMFROGGATTANDIRWIN.COM

MCLEAN-WILLIAMS MANAGEMENT

14 RATHBONE PLACE
LONDON W1T 1HT
020 7631 5385
INFO@MCLEAN-WILLIAMS.COM
WWW.MCLEAN-WILLIAMS.COM
By maintaining a select client list,
McLean-Williams Management has
formed a close working relationship
with those she and her company
represent, along with a personal
management service to that of
respected manager/agent.

MONDI ASSOCIATES LIMITED

UNIT 3 0, COOPER HOUSE
2 MICHAEL ROAD
LONDON SW6 2AD
07817 133349
INFO@MONDIASSOCIATES.COM
WWW.MONDIASSOCIATES.COM
Representing actors, actresses and young
performers, Together with creative professionals working within the theatre, musical
theatre, film, television, and commercials.

MORSE & DU FER MANAGEMENT LTD

39 LUDFORD CLOSE
WARRINGTON ROAD
CROYDON CR0 4BY
020 8941 8122
INFO@MORSEDUFER.COM
WWW.MORSEDUFER.COM
Representing actors, actresses and
directors within theatre, televison and film.
Paul du Fer has accumulated over 25 years
working in the entertainment industry.

MOUTHPIECE MANAGEMENT
PO BOX 145
INKBERROW
WORCESTERSHIRE WR7 4ZG
01527 850 149
KARIN@MOUTHPIECEMANAGEMENT.CO.UK
WWW.MOUTHPIECEMANAGEMENT.CO.UK
Mouthpiece Management represent both experienced actors and new, up and coming talent. We supply actors to theatre, film, television, commercials and for roleplay and voiceovers. All our actors can be viewed on our website www.mouthpiecemanagement.co.uk Follow our news on Facebook

MPC ENTERTAINMENT
MPC HOUSE, 15-16 MAPLE MEWS
MAIDA VALE
LONDON NW6 5UZ
020 7624 1184
INFO@MPCE.COM
WWW.MPCE.COM
MPC specialises in artist management looking after many of the top personalities in the United Kingdom. Over the past 35 years many artists have been started on the road to stardom by MPC. The policy of building new talent is one that still exists today, even though MPC has a list of household star names.

MRS JORDAN ASSOCIATES
MAYFAIR HOUSE
14 - 18 HEDDON STREET
LONDON W1B 4DA
0203 151 0710

ADMIN@MRSJORDAN.CO.UK
WWW.MRSJORDAN.CO.UK
Very small client list with no clashes of type. Check our website for list of current vacancies before contacting us. We do not represent models, support artists or anyone under 16. Please do not write or call, as you will only be asked to email. Thank you

MSFT MANAGEMENT
LONDON
AGENT@MSFTMANAGEMENT.COM
WWW.MSFTMANAGEMENT.COM
msft management is a boutique management & agency firm. We promise only to ever represent ten - fourteen actors at any given time and as a result, we pride ourselves in offering a more focused and specialized service to our clients. Another unique benefit is that msft is run as a hybrid between a production company and theatre company. This means msft offer in-house projects thought the year and invites industry professionals to our end of year showcases, which improves your chances of being seen by the right people. We specialize in getting actors theatre jobs as well as marketing our clients to television and film casting agents. Our client promise: Updated actors profile page on our wesbites, www.msftmanagement.com * CV and headshot consultancy * Discounted headshot packages * Priority castings for all msft projects * Regular industry

showcases * Original monologues written specifically for you * A guarantee to honour all client performance invitations * A monthly meeting to evaluate your progress * A six - or twelve month contract

NATASHA STEVENSON MANAGEMENT LTD
STUDIO 7C, CLAPHAM NORTH ARTS CENTRE
VOLTAIRE ROAD
LONDON SW4 6DH
020 7720 3355
INBOX@NATASHASTEVENSON.CO.UK
WWW.NATASHASTEVENSON.CO.UK
Natasha Stevenson Management was established in 1997 in London. We are not an agency where you speak to an assistants' assistant. We have a small, personal team that has been with NSM for a long time. We are proud of our client list and the many actors who have grown and stayed with us as their careers have blossomed. We know our business inside out and we work hard to support and develop the careers of our clients.

NEW FACES LTD
2ND FLOOR, THE LINEN HALL
162-168 REGENT STREET
LONDON W1B 5TB
 020 7439 6900
VAL@NEWFACESTALENT.CO.UK
WWW.NEWFACESTALENT.CO.UK
Established in 2000, New Faces is now recognised as a highly reputable casting and management agency representing a small number of extremely talented actors, presenters and specialists. We aim to give established or new artists a personal, approachable and highly professional service.

NICOLA ROBERTS MANAGEMENT
149 NELSON ROAD
LONDON
N8 9RR
020 8375 5555
INFO@NICOLAROBERTSMANAGEMENT.COM
WWW.NICOLAROBERTSMANAGEMENT.COM
NICOLA ROBERTS MANAGEMENT is a dynamic talent agency, with a fresh approach to representing actors in all areas of the performing industry including: TV, Film, Theatre, Commercials, Musical Theatre and Corporate work.

NJR MANAGEMENT
HILLTOP COTTAGE
WELLAND ROAD
UPTON UPON SEVERN WORCS WR8 0SJ
 01684 592108
NIKKI@NJRMANAGEMENT.COM
NJR Management Ltd is a well established, dynamic Actors Agency based in the Midlands. NJR Management have worked hard to pull together a team of experienced professionals of all ages. We specialise in representing Midlands based actors and presenters with extensive experience in corporate production - both live and recorded - TV, commercials, and theatre as well as the specific skills of role

playing and training. The driving force behind NJR Management is Nikki Reeves. Nikki has been based in the Midlands since 1991 and during that time she has established her reputation as a dedicated professional. She has presented numerous corporate productions, has worked extensively in training both role-playing and media training. Furthermore, as the BBC's main presenter at their training college at Wood Norton for the last eleven years no one is in a better position to understand the professional needs of the industry.

NORTH WEST ACTORS - NIGEL ADAMS
36 LORD STREET
RADCLIFFE
MANCHESTER M26 3BA
0161 724 6625
INFO@NORTHWESTACTORS.CO.UK
WWW.NORTHWESTACTORS.CO.UK
North West Actors is a vibrant and successful personal management agency run by Nigel Adams. Based in Manchester and representing actors based in (or with connections to) the North West, work is procured in all areas except extras/background. Nigel represents a broad band of male and female actors of various types, ages and ethnicities, all of whom are highly talented, motivated and reliable, and based in the North West of England OR originating from the North West and now based in London or other areas of the UK.

NORTHERN PROFESSIONALS
PO BOX 147
NORTH SHIELDS
TYNE AND WEAR NE29 9YN
01912 578635
BILL@NORTHERNPROCASTING.CO.UK
WWW.NORTHERNPROCASTING.CO.UK
We have an unbeatable reputation for supplying experienced and reliable extras for TV and Film. With over 700 extras registered with us we can cater for crowd scenes as well as supplying individual supporting and walk-on artistes. Our flexible working hours, attention to detail and many years experience will provide you with the efficient service that we know is so important.

NORTHERN STAR ACTORS AGENCY
332 ROYAL EXCHANGE
MANCHESTER
M2 7BR
0161 832 3535
MARK@NORTHERNSTARACTORS.CO.UK
We are a Manchester based Acting Agency specialising in Television and Commercial work

NORTHONE MANAGEMENT
HG08 ABERDEEN CENTRE
HIGHBURY GROVE
LONDON N5 2EA
020 7359 9666
ACTORS@NORTHONE.CO.UK
WWW.NORTHONE.CO.UK
NorthOne Management was founded as

an actor's agency in 1986. Since then its founding members have moved on, but bequeathed a wealth of accumulated experience, which the current members enjoy. It is only by the collective co-operation of the members that NorthOne flourishes, whether as an actor or an agent. This pre-requisite of co-operation and involvement, we believe, also makes the actor a more professionally aware member of the industry.

NS Artistes' Management

10 Claverdon house
Holly Bank Road
Birmingham B13 0QY
0121 684 5607
NSMANAGEMENT@FSMAIL.NET

We are an agency for talent in and around, or even links with, the Midlands area and yet we provide talent for the nation whatever the location.

Nyland Management

20 School Lane
Heaton Chapel
Stockport SK4 5DG
0161 4422224
CASTING@NYLANDMANAGEMENT.COM
WWW.NYLANDMANAGEMENT.COM

Nyland Management are based in Stockport, south of Manchester. The agency was founded over 25 years ago by Patrick Nyland, who trained as an actor at Manchester University. Over the years Patrick and the agency attained a

highly regarded position within the industry, and continue to maintain a successful working relationship with Casting Directors and Production Companies based on professional commitment and trust.

Oi Oi Agency

The Coach House, Pinewood Studios
Pinewood Road, Iver Heath
Buckinghamshire SLO ONH
01753 852326
INFO@OIOI.ORG.UK
WWW.OIOI.ORG.UK

Oi Oi represents artists of all ages and ethnic backgrounds including babies, children and adults. Our clients cover a broad spectrum of ages and looks to enable us to help with most, if not all, casting briefs. We currently have over 300 clients on our books and pride our self on having talented, professional artists of all ages and diversities.

Olivia Bell Management

189 Wardour Street
London W1F 8ZD
020 7439 3270
INFO@OLIVIA-BELL.CO.UK
WWW.OLIVIA-BELL.CO.UK

Olivia Bell Management is an independent talent management agency based in Soho, London. Representing a diverse range of clients across TV, film, music and theatre, Olivia Bell is boutique in size, but powerful in impact. The high calibre of its clients has earned the agency a strong reputation within the industry for nurturing and growing talent, in addition to managing the careers of established artists. The company firmly believes in maintaining strong relationships with its clients and selecting them not only for their all-round talent, but also for their likeable personalities. Focused on the success of all its artists' careers, the Olivia Bell Management team ensures ongoing goal plans for each individual client.

ORDINARY PEOPLE
16 CAMDEN ROAD
LONDON
NW1 9DP
020 7267 7007
INFO@ORDINARYPEOPLE.CO.UK
WWW.ORDINARYPEOPLE.CO.UK
Ordinary People were established in 1988 to meet the ever increasing demand for more ordinary - looking people within the film and photographic industries. Since then, the company has been successfully supplying artistes and models to the worlds leading photographers, advertising agencies and casting directors in TV and film.

PAUL SPYKER MANAGEMENT
1-2 HENRIETTA STREET
COVENT GARDEN
LONDON WC2E 8PS
020 7379 8181
We are a leading theatrical agency based in the heart of London's West End. Our clients work in all areas of the entertainment industry, covering all areas of live theatre, television, film and commercials. We also represent a select number of creative team clients who work internationally. We only accept written applications for representation. We try to reply to all we receive, eventually! But this can take sometime please bear with us. A stamped addressed envelope also helps!

PELHAM ASSOCIATES
THE MEDIA CENTRE
9-12 MIDDLE STREET
BRIGHTON BN1 1AL
01273 323010
AGENT@PELHAMASSOCIATES.CO.UK
WWW.PELHAMASSOCIATES.CO.UK
Agents Peter Cleall & Dione Inman. Representing actors of the highest quality for casting within all branches of the media.

PEMBERTON ASSOCIATES
193 WARDOUR STREET
LONDON W1F 8ZF
020 7734 4144
GENERAL@PERMBERTONASSOCIATES.COM
WWW.PERMBERTONASSOCIATES.COM

Pemberton Associates is an actors' agency and was established in 1989 by Barbara Pemberton. It has offices in Manchester and London and is a member of the Personal Managers' Association.

PEMBERTON ASSOCIATES (MANCHESTER OFFICE)
EXPRESS NETWORKS
1 GEORGE LEIGH STREET
MANCHESTER M4 5DL
0161 2358440
GENERAL@PERMBERTONASSOCIATES.COM

PERFORMANCE ACTORS AGENCY
137 GOSWELL ROAD
LONDON EC1V 7ET
020 7251 5716
INFO@PERFORMANCEACTORS.CO.UK
WWW.P-A-A.CP.UK
Since it was founded in 1984, Performance Actors Agency has established an outstanding reputation for providing experienced professional actors to the entertainment industry. Run by actors, for actors, Performance is recognised by directors, casting directors and producers as one of the Premiere League agencies of its kind. We represent a diverse and talented group of committed, hard working performers, and our client's CVs cover every field of the business: Film; Television; Radio; West End and major companies including The National Theatre and Royal Shakespeare Company; Regional Repertory Theatre; Commercials, Voice-Overs, Corporate Work and Role-Play.

PETER SHELDRAKE
139 LOWER RICHMOND ROAD
LONDON SW14 7HX
020 8876 9572
PSAGENT@BTINTERNET.COM
New agency formed in 2007, specialising in Theatre, TV and Films. We keep our client books to a managable number so we can ensure that each and every client gets our full attention at all times.

PICCADILLY MANAGEMENT
23 NEW MOUNT STREET
MANCHESTER M4 4DE
0161 953 4057
INFO@PICCADILLYMANAGEMENT.COM
WWW.PICCADILLYMANAGEMENT.COM
We are an established agency based in Manchester but have clients from all over the country, including London. We are always on the lookout for exciting new talent and have a strong history of providing actors for stage, film and television.

PINK OLIVE AGENCY
WIGMORE ROAD
WORTHING
WEST SUSSEX BN14 9HJ
LYN@PINKOLIVEAGENCY.COM
The Pink Olive Agency is a vibrant new agency based on the southcoast. If you are an actor in need of representation please send us your CV and headshot. lyn@pinkoliveagency.com Tel.07930 121126

PLATINUM ARTISTS
TELFORD PLAZA 2
IRONMASTERS WAY
TELFORD TF3 4NT
01952 458457
MARK@PLATINUMARTISTS.CO.UK
WWW.PLATINUMARTISTS.CO.UK
Platinum Artists is a privately owned Talent Agency based in the United Kingdom representing Actors, Actresses and Presenters for TV, Film, Radio, Theatre, Commercials and all other areas of the Media sector. Platinum Artists are currentlly accepting new applications and will be holding Open Auditions on Saturday 29th May 2010 in London. If you wish to be considered to join the Agency, please visit our website.

PRICE GARDNER MGT
PO BOX 59908
LONDON SW16 5QH
020 7610 2111
INFO@PRICEGARDNER.CO.UK
WWW.PRICEGARDNER.CO.UK
Film, TV , Theatre, Commercials, Voice Over, Radio & Musical Theatre

RBM
3RD FLOOR, 168 VICTORIA STREET
LONDON SW1E 5LB
020 7630 7733
INFO@RBMACTORS.COM
WWW.RBMACTORS.COM
RBM ACTORS is a London based talent agency representing a range of professionally trained actors and actresses in theatre, film & T.V.

REALITY CHECK MANAGEMENT LTD
PARAMOUNT BUILDING
206-212 ST JOHN STREET
LONDON EC1V 4JY
020 7324 1450
INFO@REALITYCHECK-M.COM
WWW.REALITYCHECKMANAGEMENT.COM
Reailty Check Management is a Acting, Modelling, Performers and Celebrities agency. Based in Central London W1.

REDRUSH TALENT
37 MAIN STREET
KILLINCHY
CO.DOWN BT23 6PN
02897 543272
JANICE@REDRUSHTALENT.COM
WWW.REDRUSHTALENT.COM
RedRush Talent   RedRush is a new, and new kind of, talent management resource. Founded in 2009, RedRush is an idea that grew out of my direct personal experience. As a model and as an actor in film, television and theatre over the past twenty years I've been exposed to the wide variety of creative and business dimensions of the performing and commercial arts worlds.I want to bring that experience to bear in helping fellow actors, directors, writers and other creative talents realize their commercial potential.   In addition to offering representation and counsel to actors, RedRush is dedicated to helping develop talent across a diverse range of creative disciplines. Its current roster includes actors, writers and directors (including

director Allan Gildea), radio presenters (including BBC's Conor Bradford), voice over artists including Phillip Sacramento and Dublin-based Luke Hayden, photographers (including Billy Riley) and illustrators. Janice Rush, Founder Actress Lived and worked in New York, London, Athens, Paris and Belfast...theatre training at New York's Circle in the Square, Off Boadway... film credits include three independent award winners - 'Chihuahua,' Elsewhere and The Goldfish Bowl...television credits include the recent BBC 1 drama, Cinderella and BBC Northern Ireland's I Fought The Law...commercial credits include Guinness, Ballygowan, Barry's Tea, and Progressive Building Society....currently at work on Cat Goes to London, an illustrated children's book, as well as a black comedy for the theatre.

RICHARD STONE PARTNERSHIP

2 HENRIETTA STREET
LONDON WC2E 8PS
020 7497 0849
MPOOLE@THERSP.COM
www.therichardstonepartnership.co.uk
Richard Stone, who became an agent when he returned from service as Entertainments Officer at the end of the Second World War, celebrated over 50 years in show business. Meg Poole joined him in 1975 and the company became a Partnership in 1986. The current Partners are Meg Poole and Vivienne Clore.

ROSEBERY MANAGEMENT

HOXTON HALL
130 HOXTON STREET
LONDON N1 6SH
ADMIN@ROSEBERYMANAGEMENT.COM
WWW.ROSEBERYMANAGEMENT.COM
Established in 1984, Rosebery Management has succeeded in becoming one of the most highly respected Co-operative agencies in the UK. Rosebery represents and looks after around 30 actors in theatre, television, film, commercials, radio, voice-overs and corporate work. All actors are members of 'Spotlight' and 'Equity'. Rosebery prides itself on the quality and high standards of it's Clients' work, which includes: Theatre: The Royal National Theatre, Birmingham Rep, West Yorkshire Playhouse, Mark Goucher Ltd, The Royal Court. TV: BBC 1, 2, 3 & 4, Channel 4, Channel 5, Sky, Discovery. Film: MGM Warner Bros, Labrador Films Ltd, Hammer House Of Horror, Eclectic Pictures. Radio: BBC Radio 3, 4 & 7. Commercial: Saatchi & Saatchi, Maverick Media, Rokkit, Stink, Partizan, Feel Films, Draw Pictures. Should you have any casting requirements please contact the Administrator on 020 7684 0187, and if you are seeking representation please browse our Representation page on our website at www.roseberymanagement.com.

ROWE ASSOCIATES

33 PERCY ST
LONDON W1T 2DF
01992 308519
AGENTS@GROWE.CO.UK
WWW.GROWE.CO.UK

Talent agency, representing actors, actors/musicians and musical theatre performers in the global entertainment industry, including Film, TV, Stage and Commercials.

SAINOU

10-11 LOWER JOHN STREET
LONDON W1F 9EB
020 7734 6441
OFFICE@SAINOU.COM
WWW.SAINOU.COM

With an office in the West End (London), Sainou offers personal management to actors and creatives throughout the UK, Europe and US. Established in 2009 the company has 2 agents, David Marsden and Paul Martin who have more than 20 years experience in the Entertainment and Media sector.

SANDRA GRIFFIN MANAGEMENT LTD

6 RYDE PLACE
RICHMOND ROAD
EAST TWICKENHAM TW1 2EH
020 8891 5676
OFFICE@SANDRAGRIFFIN.COM
WWW.SANDRAGRIFFIN.COM

Sandra Griffin Management Ltd was established in 1989, and represents actors and performers, in film, television, theatre, musical theatre, corporate and commercial work, voice work and presenting. Sandra Griffin and Howard Roberts are the co-directors, and share responsibility for representing all the clients.

SANDRA REYNOLDS AGENCY

SHAKESPEARE HOUSE
168 LAVENDER HILL
LONDON SW11 5TF
020 7387 5858
INFO@SANDRAREYNOLDS.CO.UK
WWW.SANDRAREYNOLDS.CO.UK

Sandra Reynolds has been established since 1977 as one of the UK's most highly respected agencies. With offices in both London and Norwich, we represent established actors, presenters, models and children for tv commercials and stills campaigns throughout the UK and worldwide. We are well-known for our friendly efficient service with most new clients and actors/models contacting us through recommendation.

SANDRA SINGER ASSOCIATES

21 COTSWOLD ROAD
WESTCLIFF-ON-SEA
ESSEX SS0 8AA
01702 331616
SANDRASINGERUK@AOL.COM
WWW.SANDRASINGER.COM

Sandra Singer Associates are one of the UK's agents for Feature Films, Film, TV and Commercials. They also supply Musical Theatre artistes to West End and

No 1 Tours mainly. They also have a few specialist clients - choreographers - Commercial Dancers. and Akil (Google him!).   They also supply clients Internationally, to USA and Germany etc. They have a personalised and very professional service to both clients, and artistes.   For more details please check our website. www.sandrasinger.com

SCOTT MARSHALL PARTNERS LTD
SUITE 954
POLAND STREET
LONDON W1F 7NJ
020 7432 7240
SMPM@SCOTTMARSHALL.CO.UK
WWW.SCOTTMARSHALL.CO.UK
Scott Marshall Partners Ltd was formed in 2002 when Amanda Evans, Suzy Kenway and Manon Palmer were invited to become directors of Scott Marshall Personal Management, which was established in 1966 by Scott Marshall. In 2003, we moved the agency in to the West End, and in 2006 moved to our current location in Little Portland Street. We are a leading theatrical agency, primarily representing actors with a small number of television directors, theatre directors and theatre creatives. Our clients work at the highest level across television, film, theatre and radio, both in the UK and overseas.

SCOTT-NIVEN ASSOCIATES
LOWER GROUND FLOOR OFFICE
205 VICTORIA RISE
LONDON SW4 0PF
THETEAM@SCOTT-NIVENASSOCIATES.COM
WWW.SCOTT-NIVENASSOCIATES.COM
Scott-Niven Associates formed in 2008. Representing professional actors for screen & stage.

SHANE COLLINS ASSOCIATES
11-15 BETTERTON STREET
COVENT GARDEN
LONDON WC2H 9BP
020 7470 8864
INFO@SHANECOLLINS.CO.UK
WWW.SHANECOLLINS.CO.UK
We represent Actors and personalities in the Entertainment Industry including Film, Television, Radio, Theatre, Musical Theatre, Voiceovers, Personal Appearances and Corporate Engagements. We work closely as a team with our actors.

SHARON FOSTER MANAGEMENT
15A HOLLYBANK ROAD
BIRMINGHAM B13 0RF
01214 434865
MAIL@SHARONFOSTER.CO.UK
WWW.SHARONFOSTER.CO.UK
Sharon Foster Management is a professional actors' agency based in Birmingham, UK, and operating nationwide. Thanks to strong links with employers both locally and nationally, the agency's actors are currently employed

countrywide in a wide range of projects, including film, television, radio, theatre, commercials and corporate work. The agency was established and is managed by Sharon Foster. Sharon's background is in theatre, production and casting. Whatever role you need to cast, Sharon Foster Management's professionalism and diverse portfolio of clients and contacts will help you to find exactly the right person.

SHEPPERD-FOX

5 MARTYR ROAD
GUILDFORD GU1 4LF
INFO@SHEPPERD-FOX.CO.UK
WWW.SHEPPERD-FOX.CO.UK

Shepperd-Fox is an established actors agency bringing a wealth of practical experience to the industry. The partners combine long term experience in theatre, television and film with strong business and relationship management skills. This ensures our clients and industry professionals are provided with in-depth appropriate high level representation and communication.

SPACE PERSONAL MANAGEMENT

PO BOX 64412
LONDON W5 9GU
020 8560 7709
KATHERINE@SPACEPERSONALMANAGEMENT.CO.UK
WWW.SPACEPERSONALMANAGEMENT.CO.UK

Representation of Professional Adult Actors and Entertainers within the Theatrical, Film and Broadcast Industries.

STAGE CENTRE MANAGEMENT LTD

41 NORTH ROAD
LONDON N7 9DP
020 7607 0872
INFO@STAGECENTRE.ORG.UK
WWW.STAGECENTRE.ORG.UK

Stage Centre Management is a cooperative actors agency based in North London. Formed in 1982, the agency represents around 25 actors across all areas of the industry. Stage Centre members regularly appear in the West End and in feature films, on UK and European theatre tours, on television and in commercials. Stage Management prides itself on a professional, personal and knowledgeable relationship with figures across the industry, whilst maintaining a friendly and supportive atmosphere between members. As an agency Stage Centre aims to represent a diverse group of actors.

STEPHANIE EVANS ASSOCIATES

RIVINGTON HOUSE
82 GREAT EASTERN STREET
LONDON EC2A 3JF
0870 609 2629
STEPH@STEPHANIE-EVANS.COM
WWW.STEPHANIE-EVANS.COM

Stephanie Evans Associates (formerly known as VocalWorks International) was founded in 2003 and came about as an extension of our work as professional performers, directors and personal managers in the business for over 25 years. Stephanie Evans Associates is a dedicated personal management run by honorable and hardworking people who are available to their clients 24/7. To which, their valued clients will attest. We always make time to regularly meet our clients at offices at the above address. At the request of our clients, we also arrange meetings at a location of our mutually convenient designation. Although we are a relatively new agency, we appreciate the importance of supplying the most adept clients for the specific work criteria and high standards of potential employers. Therefore, our client list is appropriately selective to ensure that we are fair to both our clients and employers. At present, we have clients working throughout the UK and in the USA.

STEVE DANIELS MANAGEMENT

THE OFFICE
146 RODING ROAD
LOUGHTON ESSEX IG10 3BS
0203 0077538
TALENT@STEVEDANIELSMANAGEMENT.CO.UK
WWW.TALENT@STEVEDANIELSMANAGEMENT.CO.UK
Steve Daniels Management offer a complete package with our clients primed and experienced in all areas of the Stage, Screen and Entertainment

STEVE JAMES GARRY

2 SOUTH STREET
RAMSBOTTOM
BURY BL0 0AJ
STEVEJAMESGARRY@LIVE.CO.UK
WWW.STEVEGARRY.INFO
Steve James Garry (SJG) is a new actors agency based in the north of Manchester commencing business February 2010. (SJG) uses a small client base so that 'all' clients can be carefully considered for the full list of daily breakdowns advertised through the actors Spotlight database. As an actor/agent Steve James Garry has one international independent film award and has 3 solid years experience in the independent film and corporate industries. SJG represents himself and a handful of experienced actors who are driven and passionate about their chosen professions and whom have steadfast attitudes, motives and beliefs toward sustaining careers within the performance arts.

SUSAN ANGEL &KEVIN FRANCIS LTD

1ST FLOOR 12 D'ARBLAY STREET
LONDON W1F 8DU
020 7439 3086
AGENTS@ANGELANDFRANCIS.CO.UK
WWW.ANGELANDFRANCIS.CO.UK

SUSI EARNSHAW MANAGEMENT
THE BULL THEATRE, 68 HIGH STREET
BARNET
HERTS EN5 3SJ
020 8441 5010
CASTING@SUSIEEARNSHAW.CO.UK
WWW.SUSIEEARNSHAWMANAGEMENT.COM
Susi Earnshaw Management is a
personal management representing both
adult and child performers in theatre, TV,
film, radio, commercials, corporate work
and the live entertainment industry.
Established in 1989 SEM is one of the
country's leading agencies.

SUZANN WADE
9 WIMPOLE MEWS
LONDON W1G 8PBT
020 7486 0746
WWW.SUZANNWADE.COM
We are based in London's West End and
specialise in the personal management
of talented professionals. We work with
actors to develop strategies and help
nurture their careers. Each of our clients
is unique. Our small client base allows
us to offer the very best service we can.

TAVISTOCK WOOD
45 CONDUIT STREET
LONDON W1S 2YN
020 7494 4767
INFO@TAVISTOCKWOOD.COM
WWW.TAVISTOCKWOOD.COM
We work to enhance and extend
creative opportunity, and to continually
develop the economic and cultural value
of original artistic voices. The professional expertise of Tavistock Wood is
built on years of experience both in arts
and commerce. Our principle fields of
activity are in film, theatre, television
and publishing, across all international
markets. We place a strong focus on the
management and protection of both
image rights and intellectual property
rights. Further activities include project
development, business affairs, and communications and brand advisory services.

TIM SCOTT PERSONAL MANAGEMENT
PO BOX 61776
LONDON SW1V 3UX
020 7828 3824

VINCENT SHAW ASSOCIATES LTD
51 BYRON ROAD
LONDON E17 4SN
020 8509 2211
INFO@VINCENTSHAW.COM
WWW.VSALTD.COM
VSA has a long and very fine heritage as
an agency, having been created by the
theatrical agent and impresario Vincent
Shaw back in the 1950s. Since then the
agency has maintained its position as a
top theatrical management looking after
many successful artists including the
legendary Jessie Matthews as well as
giving many industry leaders such as Bill
Kenwright an opportunity to get started
in the industry. Andy Charles took over
the agency in 2002, after working
alongside Vincent Shaw as his head

agent, and today runs VSA with fellow agent and business partner Tod Weller. Their combined experience of the industry from both sides of the fence (Andy's from his career as an actor and Tod's from his career in TV, advertising and commercial production) ensures an in depth under-standing of the demands of an ever changing business as well as an empathy and insight into the daily challenges of an artist's life. Our continued success depends on our relationships with our clients and our relationships with casting professionals – relationships we nurture and never take for granted; friendly, pro-fessional and very personal management is paramount to all that we do.

VisABLE People

P.O. Box 80
Droitwich WR9 0ZE
01905 776631
LOUISE@VISABLEMODELS.CO.UK
WWW.VISABLEPEOPLE.COM
Visable is the UK's first professional agency representing only actors and models with disabilities. VisABLE represents highly motivated individuals of all ages and disabilities but above all, abilities. Many have considerable experience as competitors in a wide variety of sports at international level, including Olympic Gold Medallists. Mainstream advertising campaigns and productions continue to be the agency's target market. Our aim is to ensure that people with disabilities are portrayed as ordinary consumers, simply individuals with spending power as shoppers, families, business people, sports enthusiasts - just part of everyday society.

W Athletic

The Hub, Fowler Avenue
IQ Farnborough Business Park
GU14 7JF
01252 302255
TALENT@WATHLETIC.COM
WWW.WATHLETIC.COM
W Athletic specialises in managing healthy talent including Models, Actors, Dancers, Acrobats, Sports, Free-Runners etc.

Waring and McKenna

11-12 Dover Street
Mayfair
London W1S 4LJ
020 7629 6444
DJ@WARINGANDMCKENNA.COM
WWW.WARINGANDMCKENNA.COM
With a focus on career progression, we aim to fully develop an actor's potential and to provide every opportunity required to achieve that end. We have strong connections throughout the industry, both in the UK and the States. Our agents work proactively and consistently with casting directors, directors and producers and we also work closely with a range of agents and managers in Los Angeles and New York. In an ever-changing world, Waring and McKenna combines cutting edge technology with a traditional one-to-one approach to personal management.

WEST CENTRAL MANAGEMENT
PANTHER HOUSE
38 MOUNT PLEASANT
LONDON WC1X 0AP
020 7833 8134
mail@westcentralmanagement.co.uk
www.westcentralmanagement.co.uk
Established in 1984. Co-operative management representing 15-20 actors. Areas of work include theatre, musicals, television, film, commercials and corporate. Members are expected to work 4 days in the office per month. We will consider postal or emailed applications (with CVs and photographs) from actors previously unknown to the agency. We will view actors' websites. We also need to see a live performance or show reel, but only after an initial meeting. We need at least two weeks notice for live shows.

WHITE STAG CASTING
7 FOUNTAINS WALK
WA3 1EU
WHITESTAG@HOTMAIL.CO.UK
WHITESTAGCASTING.CO.UK
White Stag is a small agency. We pride ourselves on the fact that we are solely for professional actors and this is our only focus. We are a growing company and hope to have a maximum of 20 actors by the end of this year. Our motto is the personal touch and this is exactly the service White Stag will offer.

Co-operative agencies

A co-operative agency is one run by actors themselves: a group of actors (usually 20 or so) working together to represent each other. Work such as answering the phone, administering the office and working contacts will be undertaken on a rota basis. Many co-operative agencies will charge commission at the lower end of the scale (closer to 10% than 20%), which can be attractive to an actor. While they can and do work, co-operative agencies may not always carry the same clout with casting directors as the more traditional agencies. However, there are advantages too: one is that members have more day-to-day involvement with their career management. Everyone in the co-op is invested in success and motivated by similar goals. Another advantage is that co-ops sometimes pursue a broader range of work, such as corporate and educational opportunities. And you're learning about and dealing with all aspects of the industry, including the casting process and even liaising with casting directors.

Think carefully about why you might want to join a co-op – that's sure to be one of the questions its existing members ask you in an interview. Don't be offended if you're asked to go through a probationary period – it's only reasonable that a group of people with a particular dynamic will want to make sure, for both parties' sake, that things will work out. Good communication between members of a co-op is vital to its success.

Most agencies will be members of the Co-operative Personal Management Association (CPMA). Founded in 2002, the CPMA works to further and promote the interests of its members. who are acting agencies located across the UK. Backed by Equity, the CPMA seeks to raise the profile of co-ops with both employers and actors and to represent the interests of co-ops with external bodies.

A-Z of Co-operative Agencies

21ST CENTURY ACTORS MANAGEMENT
BASED IN: LONDON
{T} 020 7278 3438
E-MAIL@21STCENTURYACTORS.CO.UK
WWW.21STCENTURYACTORS.CO.UK
21st Century Actor's Management co-operative agency was established in 1992 by a group of actors who wanted to wrest control of their careers from personal managers and represent each other. We are currently opening our books, for a limited time only, to a broad range of new talent. The cooperative is especially interested in applications from ethnic minority and middle-aged male actors.

1984 PERSONAL MANAGEMENT
BASED IN: LONDON
{T} 020 7251 8046
INFO@1984PM.COM
WWW.1984PM.COM
1984 is a co-operative personal management agency representing approximately 20 actors across film, theatre, television and commercials.

ACTORS ALLIANCE
BASED IN: LONDON
{T} 020 7407 6028
ACTORS@ACTORSALLIANCE.CO.UK
WWW.ACTORSALLIANCE.CO.UK
Actors alliance is a co-operative agency providing representation to its members in the entertainment industry. Our aim is provide helpful and accurate recommendations to casting professionals in the fields of film, television, theatre and corporate work.

ACTORS' CREATIVE TEAM
BASED IN: LONDON
{T} 020 7278 3388
OFFICE@ACTORSCREATIVETEAM.CO.UK
WWW.ACTORSCREATIVETEAM.CO.UK
Actors' Creative Team is a co-operative agency established in 2001 and is jointly owned and run by professional actors. Each member acts as an agent, representing colleagues and finding them work in every area of the profession.

ACTORS DIRECT
BASED IN: MANCHESTER, LEEDS, LONDON, SOUTH-WEST
{T} 0161 237 1904
INFO@ACTORSDIRECT.ORG.UK
WWW.ACTORSDIRECT.CO.UK
Founded in 1994, Actors Direct has 25 members, with roughly equal numbers of men and women, mainly based around the north-west of England. Members are expected to have excellent office skills and a strong sense of team spirit. The group does not represent under 16s or walk on artists. Actors Direct is actively seeking submissions from mixed race, oriental, black and Asian actors.

THE ACTORS' FILE

BASED IN: LONDON
{T} 020 7278 0087
MAIL@THEACTORSFILE.CO.UK
WWW.THEACTORSFILE.CO.UK

The Actors' File is a small boutique co-operative agency created 25 years ago. We do our utmost to remain competitive and accessible.

THE ACTORS' GROUP

BASED IN: MANCHESTER
{T} 0161 8344466
ENQUIRIES@THEACTORSGROUP.CO.UK
WWW.THEACTORSGROUP.CO.UK

The Actors Group was formed in 1980 and was the co-operative actors' agency outside of London. TAG (as the agency quickly became known) continues to work in all the media nationally and internationally. Since its inception the agency has provided actors for work on the stages of RSC, the RNT, The Old Vic, The Young Vic, The Royal Court and practically every regional Rep, as well as small/middle scale theatre, children's theatre and TIE, film and television. Our experienced membership ranges from young actors, to those middle-aged as well as established older actors. The age range spans 18 to 72.

ACTORS NETWORK AGENCY (ANA)

BASED IN: LONDON
{T} 020 7735 0999
INFO@ANA-ACTORS.CO.UK
WWW.ANA-ACTORS.CO.UK

ANA was established in 1985 and represents 20-30 actors in film, theatre, television and commercials.

ACTORUM

BASED IN: LONDON
{T} 020 7636 6978
INFO@ACTORUM.COM
WWW.ACTORUM.COM

Actorum was established in 1974 by Danny Schiller and Vivienne Burgess. We were the first actors' co-operative in the United Kingdom. Over 30 years on, Actorum remains the premiere co-operative agency, constantly aiming to provide a first class, personal, knowledgeable and dynamic service to the industry.

ALPHA PERSONAL MANAGEMENT

BASED IN: LONDON
{T} 020 7241 0077
ALPHA@ALPHAACTORS.COM
WWW.ALPHAACTORS.COM

Alpha Personal management was established in 1983, and is a co-operative personal management agency representing approximately 20 actors across film, theatre, television and commercials.

ARENA PERSONAL MANAGEMENT

BASED IN: LONDON
{T} 020 7278 1661
ARENAPMLTD@AOL.COM
WWW.ARENAPMLTD.CO.UK

Arena is a professional, hard-working,

actors' co-operative agency established in the 1980s. We represent professionally trained or experienced performers. We do not represent extras, models, dancers or children.

AXM

BASED IN: LONDON
{T} 020 7837 3304
INFO@AXMGT.COM
WWW.AXMGT.COM

We are a non-profit organization that exists to represent its members' interests in film, television, theatre, presentation, roleplay, voiceover and all other areas of performance arts. We are always interested in hearing from actors from all backgrounds who wish to join us.

BRIDGES: THE ACTORS' AGENCY

BASED IN: EDINBURGH
{T} 0131 226 6433
ADMIN@BRIDGESACTORSAGENCY.COM
WWW.BRIDGESACTORSAGENCY.COM

As a cooperative, Bridges: The Actors' Agency is the only one of its kind in Scotland. All of our actors are fully trained professionals with a wide variety of skills and experience in a range of areas such as theatre, TV, film, radio, stand-up comedy, voice-over work and corporate, to name but a few.

CASTAWAY ACTORS AGENCY

BASED IN: DUBLIN
{T} 353 1 6719264
CASTAWAY@CLUBI.IE
WWW.IRISH-ACTORS.COM

Founded in 1988, Castaway Actor's Agency is a not-for-profit organisation aimed at increasing the influence of individual actors over the professional management of their careers. Structured on a co-operative basis, every member plays an integral part in the running of every part of the agency.

CCM

BASED IN: LONDON
{T} 020 7278 0507
CASTING@CCMACTORS.COM
WWW.CCMACTORS.COM

Established in 1993, Ccm represents approximately 20 actors across film, theatre, television and commercials. When not working, we take turns in the office – this is normally one day a week fulfilling the following tasks: liaising with directors; submitting clients for current castings; and actively searching for opportunities within the industry.

THE CENTRAL LINE

BASED IN: NOTTINGHAM
{T} 0115 941 2937
CENTRALLINE@BTCONNECT.COM
WWW.THE-CENTRAL-LINE.CO.UK

The Central Line is a co-operative personal management agency formed in 1983 and based in Nottingham. We supply actors nationwide – most of them have London bases and are flexible and responsible.

CIRCUIT PERSONAL MANAGEMENT
BASED IN: MIDLANDS / NORTH WEST
{T} 01782 285388
MAIL@CIRCUITPM.CO.UK
WWW.CIRCUITPM.CO.UK
Circuit is an Actors' Co-operative established in 1988. Our client list is primarily in Midlands and North-West based, working throughout the UK in theatre, television, radio, voice-over, film and corporates (both video and role-play).

CITY ACTORS MANAGEMENT
BASED IN: LONDON
{T} 020 7793 9888
INFO@CITYACTORS.CO.UK
WWW.CITYACTORS.CO.UK
London's premier co-operative agency was established in 1982 and continues to thrive.

CRESCENT MANAGEMENT
BASED IN: LONDON
{T} 020 8987 0191
MAIL@CRESCENTMANAGEMENT.CO.UK
WWW.CRESCENTMANAGEMENT.CO.UK
Crescent Management is a theatrical agency dedicated to supplying professional, trained, talented actors for the stage and screen. Established since 1991 and representing approximately 25 actors.

DENMARK STREET MANAGEMENT
BASED IN: LONDON
{T} 020 7700 5200
MAIL@DENMARKSTREET.NET
WWW.DENMARKSTREET.NET
Established in 1985, Denmark Street Management has developed over the years to become one of the UK's leading co-operative agencies – specialising in providing highly skilled professional actors for theatre, film, television, commercials and radio.

DIRECT PERSONAL MANAGEMENT
{T} 020 8694 1788
DAPHNE.FRANKS@DIRECTPM.CO.UK
WWW.DIRECTPM.CO.UK
Founded in Leeds in 1985, Direct Personal Management represents a range of actors of varying ages and types. All are experienced Equity members. Our clients work in theatre, film, television, radio, voice-over , video and corporate projects. We do not represent extras or walk-ons. Many of our actors are from the North of England and we also represent actors from London and other areas including Wales. Our actors work throughout the United Kingdom and also internationally.

IML

BASED IN: LONDON

{T}020 7587 1080

INFO@IML.ORG.UK

WWW.IML.ORG.UK

ML is a co-operative actors' agency, registered as a Friendly Society. It was founded in 1980, making it one of the oldest co-ops, as well as being one of the UK's most successful.

INSPIRATION MANAGEMENT

BASED IN: LONDON

{T} 020 7704 0440

MAIL@INSPIRATIONMANAGEMENT.ORG.UK

WWW.INSPIRATIONMANAGEMENT.ORG.UK

We are an actors' co-operative agency, established in 1986, and have become one of the most respected and longest-running co-operatives in the country. Based in Islington (within easy reach of London's West End) we have over twenty members, representing a wide range of skills and experience.

NORTH OF WATFORD

{T} 01422 845361

INFO@NORTHOFWATFORD.COM

WWW.NORTHOFWATFORD.COM

North of Watford Actors' Agency is a co-operative agency representing actors living and working all over the United Kingdom.

NORTHONE MANAGEMENT

BASED IN: LONDON

{T} 020 7359 9666

ACTORS@NORTHONE.CO.UK

WWW.NORTHONE.CO.UK

NorthOne Management was founded as an actors agency in 1986. Since then its founding members have moved on, but bequeathed a wealth of accumulated experience, which the current members enjoy. It is only by the collective co-operation of the members that NorthOne flourishes, whether as an actor or an agent. This prerequisite of co-operation and involvement, we believe, also makes the actor a more professionally aware member of the industry.

NORTH WEST ACTORS

BASED IN: MANCHESTER

{T} 0161 724 6625

NIGEL.ADAMS@NORTHWESTACTORS.CO.UK

WWW.NORTHWESTACTORS.CO.UK

Based in Manchester, North West Actors represents top calibre actors based in the North West of England as well as actors native to the area but now based in London or other areas of the UK. The agency was established in January 2007 and is run by Nigel Adams, previously an actor himself for 18 years. Nigel's actors are of varying ages, types and ethnicities, all being highly talented, professional and reliable, with a formidable work ethic.

OTTO PERSONAL MANAGEMENT

BASED IN: SHEFFIELD
{T} 0114 275 2592
ADMIN@OTTOPM.CO.UK
WWW.OTTOPM.CO.UK

Otto Personal Management is an actors' co-operative management which was set up in Sheffield in 1985 and is now based in the heart of Sheffield's Cultural Quarter. Our actors have a wide and varying history in all aspects of the media industry. Theatre, Film, Television, Radio, Voice-Over, Multimedia and Corporate Videos etc.

OUR COMPANY

INFO@OUR-COMPANY.CO.UK
WWW.OUR-COMPANY.CO.UK
Website being refurbished.

PERFORMANCE ACTORS AGENCY

BASED IN: LONDON
{T} 020 7251 5716
INFO@PERFORMANCEACTORS.CO.UK
WWW.P-A-A.CO.UK

Founded in 1984, Performance Actors Agency has built an outstanding reputation of providing actors to the industry. Run by actors, for actors, Performance Actors Agency represents talented, committed and hard-working performers who have chosen to be part of a team. Our members' work includes film and television, the Royal Shakespeare Company, repertory theatre and the West End, corporate work, radio and voiceovers.

RbA MANAGEMENT

BASED IN: LIVERPOOL
{T} 0151 708 7273
INFO@RBAMANAGEMENT.CO.UK
WWW.RBAMANAGEMENT.CO.UK

Rba Management, formerly Rattlebag Actors Agency, was launched in 1995 and has grown to become one of the leading agencies in the worth of England, with credits in TV, film, commercials, theatre and radio. RbA Management is interested in hearing from professional actors with a base in the northwest of England. The agency does not deal with extra or walk-on work.

ROSEBERY MANAGEMENT

BASED IN: LONDON
{T} 020 7684 0187
EMAIL@ROSEBERYMANAGEMENT.COM
WWW.ROSEBERYMANAGEMENT.COM

Established over 25 years ago in 'Rosebery Avenue', London EC1, Rosebery Management has succeeded in becoming one of the most highly respected Co-operative agencies in the UK. Rosebery represents around 30 actors in theatre, musicals, television, film, commercials, corporate work and voice-overs. All actors are members of 'Spotlight' and 'Equity'.

STIVEN CHRISTIE MANAGEMENT

BASED IN: EDINBURGH
{T} 0131 228 4040
INFO@STIVENCHRISTIE.CO.UK
WWW.STIVENCHRISTIE.CO.UK

Formed in 1983, the business was originally called the Actors Agency. It was established by a group of young Scottish based actors who wished to learn more about the overall industry within which they were working and to aid them in this process the new agency was set up as a co-operative partnership. We promote our talent across the entire spectrum of performance media. Our clients can be found in film, television, radio, theatre, commercials, voice-over, presentation and role-play projects. The Agency is run as a commercial enterprise by the partners Douglas Stiven and Simon Christie who work from the offices located in Dunfermline and associates in Edinburgh and London.

WEST CENTRAL MANAGEMENT

BASED IN: LONDON
{T} 020 7833 8134
MAIL@WESTCENTRALMANAGEMENT.CO.UK
WWW.WESTCENTRALMANAGEMENT.CO.UK

Established in 1984. Co-operative management representing 15-20 actors. Areas of work include theatre, musicals, television, film, commercials and corporate. Members are expected to work 4 days in the office per month. Will consider attending performances at venues within Greater London with 2 weeks' notice. Accepts submissions (with CVs and photographs) from actors previously unknown to the company sent by post or email. Will also accept invitations to view individual actors' websites.

Section 3
Applying for work

Casting directors

Casting directors are employed by directors and producers to sieve through the pool of acting talent and suggest the most appropriate actors for the part. Their job is to know the acting talent inside out and to facilitate meetings between potential candidates and the director. Armed with a character breakdown, they usually work with casting agents to shortlist suitable candidates who they think will match the role's requirements and the director's expectations.

By and large, casting directors will be brought in for specific projects (eg a film or theatre production) rather than employed on ongoing contracts. There are more than 250 casting directors in the UK, some working as individuals freelancing to production companies and others as part of larger collectives or companies. Many casting directors pride themselves on an encyclopaedic knowledge of actors and are renowned for keeping detailed notes on whoever crosses their path.

In the majority of cases the casting director does not choose or have final say over who gets a role. This is up to the director and the producer. It is in the casting director's interests to be on the side of the actor, as their reputation will be consolidated by a successful casting. The vision and choices displayed by a casting director will reflect well on them and enhance their standing in the industry, just as a poor pool of talent for casting sessions can damage their credibility.

In addition to sourcing actors, a casting director is also responsible for liaising with agents, directors and actors to schedule castings. They will often sit in on the castings and may give the actor tips beforehand on what the director will be looking for. It's important to listen to these – never forget that it's usually in the casting director's interest to get you the job just as much as it is yours, and they are likely to know more about what will appeal to the director and / or producer.

Your marketing toolkit

CVs

To maximise your chances of being called in for an audition, it is vital you spend the time constructing a professional CV. While a headshot can give an employer some idea of your facial characteristics, the CV should show your versatility, experience, dependability and professionalism. Professionalism really is key here: no matter how suitable you may be for a role, a poorly spelt, structured or printed CV can quickly remove you from consideration.

The CV should start with your contact details and those of your agent if you have one. Where possible include your email address and mobile phone number, as casting directors often need to get in contact with potential cast at very short notice and a quick response time can be critical in securing an audition slot.

Next come your key physical characteristics, such as playing age, build, height, weight, hair color, eye color, ethnicity and native accent – though don't go overboard on the detail as your photograph will reveal some of it anyway. A simple statement such as 'tall with slim build' can sometimes convey more than a list of statistics.

Credits and training

After these key contact details and physical characteristics you should include your credits and training. Again, some people prefer to put training first, others credits – it's up to you. As long as each section is clearly laid out and the CV isn't too long it shouldn't matter unduly, though we'd recommend that you lead with your credits – whatever your field, any employer or agent will look for your experience above all else. The ideal CV length is one page, so if you do need to cut back on credits, omit the oldest and least prestigious.

Credits should include the role you played (put this first), the production, the director, the venue, theatre company and the date (just the year will do). The norm is to list the most recent credits first as these are the most telling and the most relevant and there's no point keeping your big guns at the foot of the CV. If you have a number of credits across different genres you might want to list them under different sections (eg film, theatre, television, radio, corporate, commercials).

Above all, get the details right: historians may have identified more than 50 variations of the name Shaxper, but in the business 'Shakespeare' is what they expect! Avoid amateur productions if possible, or at least put these below professional experience.

Remember, first impressions are hard to reverse, so keep your CV clear, focused and honest. Don't exaggerate your role and certainly don't claim experience you've never had. Sure, a credit may slip through the net but most won't. Actors, agents, directors and casting directors are continually networking, working together professionally and meeting socially. There's every chance that lies will be found out and come back to haunt you.

Your training should include the institution, the course and the dates you attended and, if relevant, any awards or distinctions you received. It's not obligatory to include referees, though if you have a particularly prestigious referee (eg a respected actor, tutor or industry professional) it may help to include them.

Other skills

Additional skills and interests can be listed in a different section. These can be useful if you have genuine skills such as sporting abilities (horse riding is the classic), musical abilities or particular interests which may be valuable to a role. If you are confident in a range of regional or national accents, list these too, but you really need to be sure of your accuracy, or you'll soon get caught out. Don't list skills you don't have – at best you'll end up looking foolish, at worst you'll earn the reputation as a chancer or a liar. Applying for work is one part of acting where your ability to pretend should be suppressed!

Each of these sections should be clearly marked, with bold section titles so the reader can quickly establish where the key information can be found. However, don't go crazy with fancy layouts, big boxes and wacky typefaces – what people want to see is the information.

Check and check again!

Before sending your CV to anyone, check the spelling and accuracy of all the information listed. Pass it to friends and family for a second opinion and further spell checking. Finally, ensure your name is clearly visible at the top of all pages. It should be clear from your layout that the document is a CV, so no need for the label "CV" anywhere – simply focus on the key information.

In general, remember the 15-second rule: that's probably how long your CV will be looked at in the first pass, and if you can get through to the second stage of a longer look, you're well on the way. Fifteen seconds might seem depressing – but think how quickly all of us form impressions of other people when we meet them.

Keep your CV simple and informative – this doesn't have to mean it's anonymous, and a good CV always reaches a balance between conveying the details of your experience and showing what sort of person you are.

Online CVs / Profiles

A number of websites offer an online CV service. Professionally formatted, these CVs or online profiles generally allow you to enter then amend your credits, training, and at least one photo. Some of these websites include your CV in an online directory that is searchable by industry professionals and can offer a good level of exposure. Online CVs, to which you can direct people either with a link via email or a URL, can reduce the laborious task of faxing and mailing out your CV. Services of this kind specifically for actors include Spotlight and Casting Call Pro.

Bear in mind that this method of communication doesn't find favour with everyone. Some people won't want to receive CVs via email, preferring the more traditional paper copy. In general, any agent or casting director who specifies that they don't want submissions by email is perhaps less likely to be well disposed to going to a website for your details. If you're a young actor and used to doing everything online, remember that not everyone in the industry does things that way – acting is a field where personal contact counts a great deal.

Covering letters

Together with your headshot and your CV, the covering letter is your calling card. As such, it's important to set the right tone and create a good impression. While it's true that a good letter can really do you favours, it's also true that a bad, poorly presented letter can result in your application being dumped in the bin. Agents, directors and casting directors receive a mountain of unsolicited approaches and won't be able to devote more than a few moments to each, therefore it's essential that you don't give them any reason to dismiss your approach.

You might think that spelling and grammar are irrelevant and the real substance is in your acting ability, but before you get to show off your talents you need to be called to audition. You'll not get that far if you have been ruled out of the selection process by writing a poorly phrased, poorly presented letter riddled with mistakes. You'll be doing yourself a serious disservice if you send off a letter that's unprofessional in appearance and content.

Given that there will be dozens, hundreds or thousands of other letters you might wonder how you can distinguish yourself, and set your submission apart from the others. The tone of a letter is one of the most important elements and yet one of the hardest to get right. You don't want to sound sycophantic, arrogant, outlandish or zany. Including a keepsake or memento or some other such wacky device might raise a momentary smile in the office, but it's also likely to land you in the bin.

Instead, take an entirely professional approach. Start by finding out the name of the person to whom you're writing, and ensuring you know how to spell it correctly. Address your contact by their full name rather than by their first name or title.

Write in the first person singular (I) and adhere to the usual rules of grammar and letter writing. A standard letter will often start with your address at the top right, then the recipient's address (at the left-hand side of the paper) with the date opposite or beneath, followed by the greeting ("Dear Matt Barnes"), the body of the letter and concluded "Yours sincerely", with a space for your signature and beneath that your name (printed). As you begin writing the body of your letter, be yourself but keep in mind that yours will be one of many and that the agent/director won't have the time or patience to read an essay. A letter should consist of a couple of clear, succinct paragraphs outlining why you are interested in the role/agency and why you think you're suitable and should be considered. Lay the text out neatly and clearly. Finally, consider inviting the recipient, if they're someone particularly influential, to an upcoming show you're in.

If you're sitting there thinking all this advice is obvious and you don't need it, remember that people overlook these watchwords time and time again – and they miss out on work because of it.

If your letter is accompanied by a headshot and CV, they'll have an idea of your look and your career to date, so don't simply parrot what the CV says. Writing a good letter is a fine line between being arid/uninformative and irritatingly verbose and/or self-aggrandising. When writing, try to think how it will come across to the reader, a person who doesn't know you. As with your CV, the letter is a balance between coming over as cold and clinical or being too gimmicky. Be to the point... but also be human. Once again, it's a good idea to run your draft by a friend or colleague for a second opinion before sending it.

Email letters

Email covering letters may lack the tactile and visual benefits of a good quality piece of letterheaded paper – but the rules of writing remain the same. Be brief and informative, explaining what you're applying for and why you'd be suitable, but don't make it sound like it's you that's the machine rather than the computer. It's worth putting your phone number in a signature at the bottom of the mail – some people like to put a voice to the applicant. Take extra care to read and spell-check an email letter, as you won't be able to beg the postman to stop it going out: pushing the button too quickly is all too easy.

If you're attaching a CV and photo, make sure you use standard file formats such as Word and JPG – never expect the recipient to be an IT expert. Most importantly, make sure they accept email submissions at all.

Headshots

The industry standard for photos is a black and white 10 x 8" (25 x 20cm) headshot taken by a professional photographer. The headshot will usually take in the top of your shoulders (but shouldn't include the rest of your body) in a natural pose straight to camera, clearly displaying your entire face. Most importantly the photo should look like you. If you can't replicate the look on the photo when you're called into audition at 6am on a Sunday then your headshot is not doing you any justice. You need a headshot which shows the casting director exactly what you look like. If you have a birthmark, mole or wrinkle don't try and edit it out, embrace your individuality and let your headshot provide the casting director with an honest representation of who you are.

Choosing a photographer

A good photographer may well cost in excess of £250 for a session (and don't forget to check if they're VAT registered), so this is not something to take lightly. It may sound expensive but it really does need to be done properly. Before calling a photographer check their website to see if they offer any discounts to students, recent graduates, or Equity, Spotlight or Casting Call Pro members.

Word-of-mouth recommendation counts for a lot – assuming there's no commission involved, actors will only refer photographers whose work they're happy with. Ask other actors where they've had their headshots done, see which names crop up again and again and look out for those who offer a professional, friendly service at competitive rates. In addition, use online and offline directories to search for examples of photographers' work, their prices and their location. These days you'll find that most photographers and studios have a website with examples of their work which you can browse before parting with any cash. If you are considering going to a studio ask which photographer you'll be working with and try to see examples of their work. Taking an actor's headshot is a pretty specific skill and something entirely different from modelling shots or wedding photography. Make sure your photographer knows what taking an actor's headshot involves and always ask to see examples of past work.

A great way to choose a photographer is to visit Casting Call Pro's resources section at **www.uk.castingcallpro.com/resources.php**.

What is included
When negotiating a fee – and it is worth an initial approach to see if there's room for negotiation – remember to factor in the number of shots the photographer will take, the number of prints included and the cost of extra copies: you don't want to be disappointed to receive five prints when you'd been expecting ten.

The photographer will own the rights to any of the photos they take of you, even though you pay for the initial session – another good reason to check how many prints you will get, as you are likely to have to pay for extra copies. Check at the start whether the photographer's charges for these are competitive. If you want to reproduce the picture in any form (eg online, in Spotlight, at Casting Call Pro or as publicity for a show) you will need to get permission from your photographer. They should also be credited whenever you display or print the picture: this is a legal obligation.

During the session
Make sure you get a good night's sleep before the session and arrive wearing clothes which make you feel comfortable, confident and relaxed. Ensure the clothes don't distract from your face (no loud shirts or patterned blouses). You may consider taking a collection of tops to ensure they capture the right 'you'. Don't wear too much make-up and don't get your hair cut the day before – give a new cut time to settle in. It is also sensible to avoid props, backgrounds and accessories – in fact, avoid anything which draws attention away from your face. Most good photographers will be able to advise you on such things, so do listen to them, as the good ones will have been doing this for many years.
Do make sure you look clearly at the camera, particularly so that your eyes can be seen fully – though don't stare or look vacant, of course! Your eyes are like the style in which you write your covering letter –

they reveal a lot of your personality at a glance. Aim for a hint of a smile rather than something too full-on, otherwise it will come across as a bit 'too much' and perhaps mean your eyes are less noticeable.

Opinions differ on whether natural or artificial light works best, but many casting directors will prefer the former. Discuss it with your photographer – some will even take your picture out of doors.

Choosing a shot

When choosing a shot select one which looks most like you and which you think best reflects your look and talents. Ask the opinion of people you trust. While family and friends can be helpful and supportive, they may not be the best judges; better to ask fellow actors, your agent or the photographer.

If you've been given a digital image, check the size of the file: don't go emailing huge files of more than 1Mb to people as it can slow up their connection or go over their storage limit. If you're not confident with these technicalities, ask the photographer.

A photographer's tips

Professional headshot photographer Claire Grogan
(www. clairegrogan.co.uk) offers some useful pointers.

As an ex-actor myself I understand only too well the importance we all place on our headshots. We search for that elusive shot, the one that utterly captures our personality and uniqueness, the photo that covers every possible casting and makes us look absolutely fantastic! A lot to ask for, I know, but here are a few points to consider.

When choosing your photographer make sure you look at lots of different examples of their work and then choose one whose photos you really like with a style that you feel would suit you. Chat to them first on the phone and find out costs, location, how long the session times are and whether there's anywhere to change tops or adjust your hair/make up etc.

In terms of the film versus digital question, there's not a huge difference; both are great for Spotlight. Remember that final images from a film shoot can also be put on CD as a digital scan and retouched if necessary – just ask your photographer if they can do this for you.

When deciding what to wear for your main shot choose a couple of fairly neutral/classic tops that you feel good in. Think carefully and honestly about your casting potential so you can wear a couple of other appropriate things to subtly suggest different looks such as professional/gritty/romantic etc. These work well for additional photos on your Spotlight portfolio. For females I recommend a fairly natural make-up to start with and then add more if you want a slightly more glam look later in the shoot. For males, just a bit of cover-up if you need it on the odd blemish or under-eye shadows.

Prepare yourself well for the shoot and try to get a good night's sleep – you won't get the best results if you turn up bleary eyed! Try as much as possible to relax and be yourself during the shoot; that way you should end up with some great shots to choose from.

A-Z of photographers

10 OUT OF 10 PHOTOGRAPHY
BASED IN: LONDON
{T} 08451 235664
PAULJNEED@HOTMAIL.COM
WWW.PAULJNEED.CO.UK

10BY8
BASED IN: BUCKINGHAMSHIRE
{T} 07710 780152
RICHARD.WILLIAMS@10BY8.COM
WWW.10BY8.COM

3IIMAGES PHOTOGRAPHY STUDIO
BASED IN: LEICESTER
{T} 01162 625881
INFO@3IIMAGES.COM
WWW.3IIMAGES.COM

AA TRUE PHOTOGRAPHY
BASED IN: GATESHEAD
{T} 01914 910108
TRUE@BLUEYONDER.CO.UK
WWW.TRUESTILLS.COM

ACQUIRE STUDIO
BASED IN: LONDON
{T} 07723 534344
AARON@AARONNGUYENLU.CO.UK
WWW.ACQUIRESTUDIO.CO.UK

ACTOR FOCUS
BASED IN: LONDON
{T} 07530 530343
ACTORFOCUS@LIVE.CO.UK
WWW.ACTORFOCUS.CO.UK

ACTOR SUCCESS
BASED IN: BUCKINGHAMSHIRE
{T} 01753 650939
INFO@ACTORSUCCESS.CO.UK
WWW.ACTORSUCCESS.CO.UK

ACTORHEADSHOTS.CO.UK
BASED IN: LONDON
{T} 07740 507970
INFO@ACTORHEADSHOTS.CO.UK
WWW.ACTORHEADSHOTS.CO.UK

ACTORS HEADSHOTS
BASED IN: WIGAN
{T} 07977 045899
MJOBRIEN123@BTINTERNET.COM
WWW.ACTORSHEADSHOTS.EU

ACTORS ONE-STOP SHOP
BASED IN: LONDON
{T} 01617 737670
PHOTOS@ACTORSONE-STOPSHOP.COM
WWW.ACTORSONE-STOPSHOP.COM

ACTORS WORLD PHOTOGRAPHIC
BASED IN: LONDON
{T} 02089 982579
PHOTO@ACTORS-WORLD-PRODUCTION.COM
WWW.ACTORS-WORLD-PRODUCTION.COM

ADAM MATHESON PHOTOGRAPHY
BASED IN: DUNBARTONSHIRE
{T} 07742 167229
ENQUIRY@MATHESONPHOTO.COM
WWW.MATHESONPHOTO.COM

ADRIAN QUESTER PHOTOGRAPHY
BASED IN: LONDON
{T} 07786 448540
ADRIAN.QUESTER@GMAIL.COM
WWW.PBASE.COM/ADRIANQUESTER/PORTFOLIO

AHB PHOTOGRAPHY
BASED IN: LONDON
{T} 07957 101333
AHBASIT@GMAIL.COM
WWW.AHBASIT.COM

AJG PHOTOGRAPHY
BASED IN: EDINBURGH
{T} 07931 500679
INFO@AJGPHOTOGRAPHY.CO.UK
WWW.AJGPHOTOGRAPHY.CO.UK

ALAN McCREDIE PHOTOGRAPHY
BASED IN: EDINBURGH
{T} 07720 330604
ALAN@ALANMC.CO.UK
WWW.ALANMC.CO.UK

ALAN STRUTT
BASED IN: LONDON
{T} 02072 752727
ALANSTRUTT@YAHOO.COM
WWW.ALANSTRUTT.COM

ALANDINO STUDIO
BASED IN: LONDON
{T} 07765 966181
ALANDINOSTUDIO@YAHOO.COM
WWW.ANDRESLANDINO.COM

ALASTAIR WIGHT PHOTOGRAPHY
BASED IN: EDINBURGH
{T} 07985 558143
ALASTAIRWIGHT@GOOGLEMAIL.COM
WWW.ALASTAIRWIGHT.COM

ALEX BRENNER STAGE PHOTOGRAPHY
BASED IN: LONDON
{T} 07967 322704
INFO@ALEXBRENNER.CO.UK
WWW.ALEXBRENNER.CO.UK

ALEXIS HEADSHOTS
BASED IN: MANCHESTER
{T} 07748 871512
ALEXIS@ALEXISHEADSHOTS.CO.UK
WWW.ALEXISHEADSHOTS.CO.UK

ALISTAIR GUY PHOTOGRAPHY
BASED IN: LONDON
{T} 02074 196019
INFO@ALISTAIRGUY.COM
WWW.ALISTAIRGUY.COM

ALISTAIR HUGHES
BASED IN: LONDON
{T} 02089 801224
ALISTAIR@ALISTAIRHUGHES.CO.UK
WWW.ALISTAIRHUGHES.CO.UK

ALVARO MARI-THOMPSON
BASED IN: LONDON
{T} 07968 928640
ALVARO@HAUSHINKA.COM
WWW.ALVAROMARITHOMPSON.COM

ALWAYS PHOTOGRAPHY
BASED IN: RENFREWSHIRE/GLASGOW
{T} 01415 851781
INFO@ALWAYSPHOTOGRAPHY.CO.UK
WWW.ALWAYSPHOTOGRAPHY.CO.UK

AM-LONDON
BASED IN: LONDON
{T} 02087 350540
CASEY@AM-LONDON.COM
WWW.AM-LONDON.COM

AMAR DAVED PHOTOGRAPHY
BASED IN: LUTON
{T} 07763 620266
ADAVED@MAC.COM
WWW.AMARDAVEDPHOTOGRAPHY.CO.UK

AMZI PHOTOGRAPHY
BASED IN: LONDON
{T} 02081 239988
CONTACT@AMZIPHOTOGRAPHY.COM
WWW.AMZIPHOTOGRAPHY.COM

ANDRAS P KOVACS
BASED IN: LONDON
{T} 07919 536620
ANDRAS@ANDRASPKOVACS.COM
WWW.ANDRASPKOVACS.COM

ANDREW CHAPMAN PHOTOGRAPHY
BASED IN: SHEFFIELD
{T} 01142 663579
ANDREW@CHAPMANPHOTOGRAPHER.ECLIPSE.CO.UK
WWW.ANDREWSPHOTOS.CO.UK

ANDREW H WILLIAMS PHOTOGRAPHY
BASED IN: ESSEX
{T} 07958 577457
INFO@ANDREWHWILLIAMS.CO.UK
WWW.ANDREWHWILLIAMS.CO.UK

ANDY THORNHILL PHOTOGRAPHY
BASED IN: LONDON
{T} 07918 720744
ANDYTHORNHILLPHOTO@MAC.COM
WWW.SHOTBYANDY.COM

ANGUS DEUCHAR PHOTOGRAPHER
BASED IN: LONDON
{T} 07973 600728
ANGUS@ACTORSPHOTOS.CO.UK
WWW.ACTORSPHOTOS.CO.UK

ANNA HULL PHOTOGRAPHY
BASED IN: LONDON
{T} 02074 985023
INFO@ANNAHULLPHOTOGRAPHY.COM
WWW.ANNAHULLPHOTOGRAPHY.COM

ANNA MOODY PHOTOGRAPHY
BASED IN: LONDON/LIVERPOOL
{T} 07966 187662
ANNAEMOODY@LIVE.CO.UK
WWW.ANNAMOODYPHOTOGRAPHY.CO.UK

ARNETT-PHOTOGRAPHY
BASED IN: LONDON
{T} 07951 991530
ANETPHOTOGRAPHY@AIM.COM
WWW.ARNETT-PHOTOGRAPHY.COM

ARRANCORBETT.CO.UK
BASED IN: LONDON
{T} 02081 235609
ARRAN@ARRANCORBETT.CO.UK
WWW.ARRANCORBETT.CO.UK/PHOTOGRAPHY

THE-ARTYARD
BASED IN: BEDFORD
{T} 07764 497206
LOUGIRLING@HOTMAIL.COM
WWW.THE-ARTYARD.COM

ATTON CONRAD. PHOTOGRAPHER
BASED IN: LONDON
{T} 07834 764441
CONRAD@ATTONCONRAD.COM
WWW.ATTONCONRAD.COM

AVA DE SOUZA
BASED IN: LONDON
{T} 02083 929093
AVASELLWOOD@AOL.COM
WWW.AVADESOUZA.CO.UK

AVOCADO PORTRAITS
BASED IN: GLASGOW
{T} 01414 162416
INFO@AVOCADO-PORTRAITS.COM
WWW.AVOCADO-PORTRAITS.COM

AW HEADSHOTS
BASED IN: LONDON
{T} 07816 317038
CONTACT@AWHEADSHOTS.COM
WWW.AWHEADSHOTS.COM

AXIS DIGITAL PHOTOGRAPHY
BASED IN: BOLTON
{T} 01204 460763
AXISDIGITALPHOTOGRAPHY@HOTMAIL.COM
WWW.AXIS-DIGITAL-PHOTOGRAPHY.COM

BAKER ASHTON PHOTOGRAPHY
BASED IN: LONDON
{T} 07858 345775
BAKERASHTON89@HOTMAIL.COM
WWW.BAKERASHTONPHOTOGRAPHY.COM

BECKY MAYNES PHOTOGRAPHY
BASED IN: LONDON
{T} 07958 548403
BECKY@BECKYMAYNES.COM
WWW.BECKYMAYNES.COM

BECKY'S PHOTOGRAPHY
BASED IN: LONDON
{T} 07958 548403
BECKYMAYNES@HOTMAIL.COM
WWW.BECKYMAYNES.COM

BEN BROOMFIELD PHOTOGRAPHY
BASED IN: LONDON
{T} 07734 852620
BEN.BROOMFIELD@GMAIL.COM
WWW.BENBROOMFIELD.COM

BEN CARPENTER PHOTOGRAPHY
BASED IN: LONDON
{T} 07505 442829
MAIL@BENCARPENTERPHOTOGRAPHY.COM
WWW.BENCARPENTERPHOTOGRAPHY.COM

BEN JACKSON PHOTOGRAPHY
BASED IN: LONDON
{T} 07753 613320
BENJACKSON40@AOL.COM
WWW.BENJACKSONPHOTOGRAPHY.COM

BEN RECTOR PHOTOGRAPHY
BASED IN: ESSEX
{T} 07770 467791
BEN@BENRECTOR.COM
WWW.BENRECTOR.COM

BEN ROBERTS PHOTOGRAPHY
BASED IN: BOURNEMOUTH
{T} 07980 692109
BEN_ROBERTS@MAC.COM
WWW.BENROBERTSPHOTOGRAPHY.COM

BETTINA STRENSKE
BASED IN: LONDON
{T} 07973 331097
INFO@VIBRANTPICTURES-AGENCY.CO.UK
WWW.VIBRANTPICTURES-AGENCY.CO.UK

BLAKE LEE
BASED IN: LONDON
{T} 07725 464286
DAVIDBLAKELEY@MAC.COM
WWW.DAVIDBLAKELEY.CO.UK

BLOOMING PHOTOGRAPHY STUDIOS
BASED IN: GLOUCESTERSHIRE
{T} 07858 775922
BEN@BLOOMINGPHOTOGRAPHY.CO.UK
WWW.BLOOMINGPHOTOGRAPHY.CO.UK

BLUESDEN PHOTOGRAPHY
BASED IN: WEST SUSSEX
{T} 07588 762853
CONTACT@BLUESDENPHOTOGRAPHY.COM
WWW.BLUESDENPHOTOGRAPHY.COM

BOLTON KING PHOTOGRAPHY
BASED IN: LONDON
{T} 07780 866082
GEORGINABOLTONKING@GMAIL.COM
WWW.BOLTONKINGPHOTOGRAPHY.COM

BOUTIQUE STUDIO
BASED IN: LONDON
{T} 02076 362625
INFO@THEBOUTIQUE.TV
WWW.THEBOUTIQUE.TV

BRANDON BISHOP PHOTOGRAPHY LTD
BASED IN: LONDON
{T} 02072 757468
BRANDONBISHOPPHOTOGRAPHY@YAHOO.CO.UK
WWW.BRANDONBISHOPPHOTOGRAPHY.COM

BRENDAN BISHOP PHOTOGRAPHY
BASED IN: BRIGHTON
{T} 07917 808284
BRENDAN@CORSAIRFILMS.COM
WWW.BRENDANBISHOP.COM

BRENDAN HARRINGTON PHOTOGRAPHY
BASED IN: COUNTY DOWN
{T} 02830 266408
BRENDANHARRINGTON@BTINTERNET.COM
WWW.BRENDANHARRINGTONPHOTOGRAPHY.COM

BRENT HELSEL PHOTOGRAPHIE
BASED IN: LONDON
{T} 18886 882012
BRENT@BRENTHELSEL.COM
WWW.BRENTHELSEL.COM

BRIAN BAKER PHOTOGRAPHY
BASED IN: ESSEX
{T} 01708 701448
BRIANBAKERPHOTOGRAPHY@NTLWORLD.COM
WWW.BRIANBAKERPHOTOGRAPHY.CO.UK

BRIAN TARR PHOTOGRAPHY
BASED IN: CARDIFF
{T} 02920 498601
BRIAN.TARR@NTLWORLD.COM
WWW.BRIANTARR.CO.UK

BRIDGET JONES
BASED IN: LONDON
{T} 02088 838775
BRIDGETJONES88@BTINTERNET.COM
WWW.BRIDGETJONESPHOTOGRAPHY.CO.UK

BRUCE SMITH PHOTOGRAPHER
BASED IN: LIVERPOOL
{T} 01514 760432
B.S@MAC.COM
WWW.BRUCESMITHPHOTOGRAPHER.COM

BULL ON THE MOON STUDIOS
BASED IN: LONDON
{T} 07748 414887
INFO@BULLONTHEMOON.COM
WWW.BULLONTHEMOON.COM

BUTLERIMAGE
BASED IN: HAMPSHIRE
{T} 07515 901954
STUDIO@BUTLERIMAGE.CO.UK
WWW.BUTLERIMAGE.CO.UK

C J WILLIAMS PHOTOGRAPHY
BASED IN: LONDON
{T} 02087 588413
TERRY@CJWILLIAMS.COM
WWW.CJWILLIAMS.COM

CAMERON MCNEE PHOTOGRAPHY
BASED IN: LONDON
{T} 07876 560022
CAMERONMCNEE@HOTMAIL.COM
WWW.CAMANDDOM.COM

CARL PROCTOR PHOTOGRAPHY
BASED IN: LONDON
{T} 02076 810034
CARLPHOTOS@BTCONNECT.COM
WWW.CARLPROCTORPHOTOGRAPHY.COM

CAROLE LATIMER /PHOTOGRAPHY
BASED IN: LONDON
{T} 02077 279371
CAROLE.LATIMER@FREENET.CO.UK
WWW.CAROLELATIMER.COM

CAROLINE WEBSTER PHOTOGRAPHY
BASED IN: LONDON
{T} 07867 653019
CAROLINE@CAROLINEWEBSTER.CO.UK
WWW.CAROLINEWEBSTER.CO.UK

CAROLINEPHOTOS
BASED IN: SURREY
{T} 01276 857633
INFO@CAROLINEPHOTOS.COM
WWW.CAROLINEPHOTOS.COM

THE CASTING DUO
BASED IN: EAST SUSSEX
{T} 01323 482292
THECASTINGDUO@HOTMAIL.COM
WWW.THE-CASTING-DUO.COM

CASTING IMAGE
BASED IN: LONDON
{T} 07905 311408
PHOTO@CASTINGIMAGE.COM
WWW.CASTINGIMAGE.COM

CATHERINE SHAKESPEARE LANE
BASED IN: LONDON
{T} 02072 267694
CAT@CSL-ART.CO.UK
WWW.CSL-ART.CO.UK

CATRIN ARWEL PHOTOGRAPHY
BASED IN: LONDON
{T} 07866 717442
CATRINARWELPHOTOGRAPHY@YAHOO.CO.UK
WWW.CATRINARWELPHOTOGRAPHY.COM

CHARLOTTE STEEPLES PHOTOGRAPHY
BASED IN: LONDON
{T} 07764 604537
CHARLOTTE@CHARLOTTESTEEPLES.CO.UK
WWW.CHARLOTTESTEEPLES.CO.UK

CHRIS BAKER PHOTOGRAPHER
BASED IN: LONDON
{T} 02084 413851
CHRIS@CHRISBAKERPHOTOGRAPHER.COM
WWW.CHRISBAKERPHOTOGRAPHER.COM

CHRIS BARBER MEDIA
BASED IN: BIRMINGHAM
{T} 07922 594848
STUDIO@CHRISBARBERMEDIA.COM
WWW.CHRISBARBERMEDIA.COM

CHRIS JENKINS PHOTOGRAPHY
BASED IN: LONDON
{T} 07791 391870
CHRISJENKINS87@GMAIL.COM
WWW.WIX.COM/CJENKO87/CHRIS-JENKINS-PHOTOGRAPHY

CHRIS MOCK PHOTOGRAPHY
BASED IN: LONDON
{T} 07811 174247
C.MOCK@NTLWORLD.COM
WWW.CHRISMOCKPHOTOS.CO.UK

CHRIS SAUNDERS
BASED IN: SHEFFIELD
{T} 01142 631642
CHRISMSAUNDERS@HOTMAIL.COM
WWW.CHRISMSAUNDERS.COM

CHRISTIE GOODWIN PHOTOGRAPHY
BASED IN: SURREY
{T} 07799 174199
CHIEF@CCPHOTOART.BIZ
WWW.CHRISTIEGOODWIN.COM

CHRISTOPHER HOLMES PHOTOGRAPHY
BASED IN: LONDON
{T} 01539 730064
CHRISHOLMESPHOTO@BTINTERNET.COM
WWW.CHRISHOLMESPHOTO.CO.UK

CHRISTOPHER PERKINS PHOTOGRAPHY
BASED IN: CHESHIRE
{T} 07803 507150
MAIL@CHRISTOPHER-PERKINS.COM
WWW.CHRISTOPHER-PERKINS.COM

CHRISTOPHERNICHOLSON.COM
BASED IN: LONDON
{T} 07956 466138
INFO@CHRISTOPHERNICHOLSON.COM
WWW.CHRISTOPHERNICHOLSON.COM

CHUCK DOUGLAS PHOTOGRAPHY
BASED IN: LONDON
QUERY@CHUCKDOUGLAS.COM
WWW.CHUCKDOUGLAS.COM

CLAES GELLERBRINK PHOTOGRAPHY
BASED IN: LONDON
{T} 07914 897647
POSTMASTER@CLAESGELLERBRINK.CO.UK
WWW.CLAESGELLERBRINK.CO.UK

CLAIRE CURTIS PHOTOGRAPHY
BASED IN: BIRMINGHAM
{T} 07787 556573
CLAIRIEJ@HOTMAIL.CO.UK
WWW.CLAIRECURTIS.CO.UK

CLAIRE GROGAN PHOTOGRAPHY
BASED IN: LONDON
{T} 02072 721845
CLAIRE@CLAIREGROGAN.CO.UK
WWW.CLAIREGROGAN.CO.UK

CLICK2PHOTO
BASED IN: LONDON
{T} 02082 300505
CLICK2PHOTO@GMAIL.COM
WWW.CLICK2PHOTO.CO.UK

CLIFTON PHOTOGRAPHIC COMPANY
BASED IN: BRISTOL
{T} 01179 098985
ED@CLIFTONPHOTO.CO.UK
WWW.CLIFTONPHOTO.CO.UK

CLIVE MOORE PHOTO
BASED IN: LONDON
{T} 07788 815649
CLIVELYUK@YAHOO.CO.UK
WWW.CLIVEMOORE.COM

COLIN HOCKLEY PHOTOGRAPHY
BASED IN: MIDDLESEX
{T} 02089 548415
COLIN@COLINHOCKLEYPHOTOGRAPHY.CO.UK
WWW.COLINHOCKLEYPHOTOGRAPHY.CO.UK

CONOR OGLE PHOTOGRAPHY
BASED IN: LONDON
{T} 07768 394275
CONOR@CMOGLE.COM
WWW.CMOGLE.COM

CORPHOTO
BASED IN: BRISTOL
{T} 07780 608382
RACHEL@CORPHOTO.CO.UK
WWW.CORPHOTO.CO.UK

CRAZYFACES PROJECT
BASED IN: LONDON
{T} 02088 891907
HEADSHOT.FREE@GOOGLEMAIL.COM
WWW.CRAZYFACESPROJECT.INFO

CRUSHED APPLE PHOTOGRAPHY
BASED IN: LIVERPOOL
{T} 07542 906051
INFO@CRUSHEDAPPLE.CO.UK
WWW.CRUSHEDAPPLE.COM

CT IMAGES
BASED IN: BOLTON
{T} 01204 386871
INFO@CTIMAGES.CO.UK
WWW.CTIMAGES.CO.UK

CURRAN MATTHEWS PHOTOGRAPHY
BASED IN: LONDON
{T} 02089 923242
INFO@CURRANMATTHEWS.COM
WWW.CURRANMATTHEWS.COM

DAISY DAISY
BASED IN: OXFORDSHIRE
{T} 07815 294033
BUNCH-OF-DAISIES@HOTMAIL.COM
WWW.DAISY-DAISY.NET

DAN HARWOOD-STAMPER
BASED IN: HERTFORDSHIRE
{T} 01442 242410
DAN_STAMPER@HOTMAIL.COM
WWW.DANHARWOODSTAMPER.CO.UK

DANIEL BUXTON PHOTOGRAPHY
BASED IN: STRATFORD-UPON-AVON
{T} 01789 771331
STUDIO@DANIELBUXTON.CO.UK
WWW.DANIELBUXTON.CO.UK

DANIEL GREEN PHOTOGRAPHIC SERVICES
BASED IN: ESSEX
{T} 01702 213060
DAN@DANIELGREENPHOTOGRAPHIC.CO.UK
WWW.DANIELGREENPHOTOGRAPHIC.CO.UK

DANIEL SUTKA
BASED IN: LONDON
{T} 07737 770571
PHOTO@DANIELSUTKA.COM
WWW.DANIELSUTKA.COM

DANIEL HERENDI PHOTOGRAPHY
BASED IN: LONDON
{T} 07871 792327
INFO@DANIELHERENDI.COM
WWW.DANIELHERENDI.COM

DANCESCENE PHOTOGRAPHIC
BASED IN: SURREY
{T} 01737 552874
DANCESCENE.PHOTOGRAPHIC@SUPANET.COM
WWW.DANCESCENEPHOTOGRAPHIC.CO.UK

DARREN BAKER PHOTOGRAPHY
BASED IN: READING
{T} 01189 321780
DARRENBAKERPHOTO@MAC.COM
WWW.DARRENBAKERPHOTOGRAPHY.COM

DAVE BRASSINGTON
BASED IN: RUGBY
{T} 07809 548397
P1PPL@YAHOO.COM
WWW.DAVEBRASSINGTON.CO.UK

DAVEY ROSS PHOTOGRAPHER
BASED IN: LONDON
{T} 07850 949250
DAVID@DAVIXMEDIA.COM
WWW.DAVIDROSSPHOTOGRAPHY.CO.UK

DAVID BROOKS PHOTOGRAPHER
BASED IN: LONDON
{T} 02074 822465
DAVIBROOKS75@HOTMAIL.COM
WWW.MYSPACE.COM/DAVIDBROOKSPHOTO

DAVID CALVERT
BASED IN: HERTFORDSHIRE
{T} 01279 843050
INFO@CALVERT.BIZ
WWW.CALVERT.BIZ

DAVID CHARLES PHOTOGRAPHY
BASED IN: NOTTINGHAMSHIRE
{T} 01636 819548
INFO@DAVIDCHARLESFOTO.COM
WWW.DAVIDCHARLESFOTO.COM

DAVID JAMES PHOTOGRAPHY
BASED IN: LONDON
{T} 07808 597362
INFO@DAVIDJAMESPHOTOS.COM
WWW.DAVIDJAMESPHOTOS.COM

DAVID KAY PHOTOGRAPHY
BASED IN: LONDON
{T} 07961 116218
INFO@DAVIDKAYPHOTOGRAPHY.CO.UK
WWW.DAVIDKAYPHOTOGRAPHY.CO.UK

DAVID LAWRENCE PHOTO
BASED IN: LONDON
{T} 02088 582820
DAVID@DAVIDLAWRENCEPHOTO.CO.UK
WWW.DAVIDLAWRENCEPHOTO.CO.UK

DAVID LOWDELL PHOTOGRAPHY
BASED IN: BRADFORD
{T} 01274 690301
DAVID@DLPBRADFORD.COM
WWW.DLPBRADFORD.COM

DAVID PETERS DIGITAL
BASED IN: WOLVERHAMPTON
{T} 01902 397739
DP@DAVIDPETERS.CO.UK
WWW.DAVIDPETERS.CO.UK

DAVID PRICE PHOTOGRAPHY
BASED IN: LONDON
{T} 07950 542494
INFO@DAVIDPRICEPHOTOGRAPHY.CO.UK
WWW.DAVIDPRICEPHOTOGRAPHY.CO.UK

DAVID WILLIAM EDWARDS
BASED IN: LONDON
{T} 07905 384803
MAIL@DAVIDWILLIAMEDWARDS.CO.UK
WWW.DAVIDWILLIAMEDWARDS.CO.UK

DAVISON PICTURES
BASED IN: LONDON
{T} 02085 797006
ADMIN@DAVISONPICTURES.CO.UK
WWW.DAVISONPICTURES.CO.UK

DEFENSIVE MEDIA
BASED IN: SURREY
{T} 07826 520312
PHOTO@MIKEHOLDSWORTH.COM
WWW.MIKEHOLDSWORTH.COM

DEPARTMENT-F
BASED IN: SURREY
{T} 02086 680493
RUSS.BRENNAN@LIVE.CO.UK
WWW.MYSPACE.COM/DARKDUKEUK

DEREK BROWN PHOTOGRAPHY
BASED IN: LONDON
{T} 02084 886856
CASTCALLPRO@DEREKBROWN.CO.UK
WWW.DEREKBROWN.CO.UK

DEVELOPING PERCEPTIONS PHOTOGRAPHY
BASED IN: ABERDEENSHIRE
{T} 07531 302608
ANDREW@DEVELOPINGPERCEPTIONS.CO.UK
WWW.HEADSHOTS.DEVELOPINGPERCEPTIONS.CO.UK

DGPHOTOGRAPHIC.COM
BASED IN: LONDON
{T} 07855 907893
DGPHOTOGRAPHIC@GMAIL.COM
WWW.DGPHOTOGRAPHIC.COM

DIGITAL PHOTOGRAPHY BY ROB HOLDING
BASED IN: CAMBRIDGE
{T} 01954 719629
ROB@ROBHOLDING.CO.UK
WWW.ROBHOLDING.CO.UK

DOUBLENEGATIVE
BASED IN: BUCKINGHAMSHIRE
{T} 01494 580004
FARENHEIGHT451@NTLWORLD.COM
WWW.DOUBLENEGATIVE.BIZ

DOUGLAS KURN
BASED IN: SURREY
{T} 07711 545813
DOUG@DOUGLASKURN.COM
WWW.DOUGLASKURN.COM

DURHAM PHOTOGRAPHICS
BASED IN: DURHAM
{T} 07590 561536
MATT@DURHAMPHOTOGRAPHICS.CO.UK
WWW.DURHAMPHOTOGRAPHICS.CO.UK

EDINBURGH HEAD SHOTS
BASED IN: EDINBURGH
{T} 07756 178947
PICS@JOHNNEED.CO.UK
WWW.JOHNNEED.CO.UK

DYLAN BAKER CREATIVE PHOTOGRAPHY
BASED IN: DURHAM
{T} 01913 845600
DYLAN@DYLANBAKER.CO.UK
WWW.DYLANBAKER.CO.UK

EDWARD SHAW
BASED IN: BIRMINGHAM
{T} 07904 919223
ED@EDWARDSHAW.CO.UK
WWW.EDWARDSHAW.CO.UK

EAMON KENNEDY
BASED IN: LONDON
{T} 07949 581069
EPKFOTO@GMAIL.COM
WWW.EAMON-KENNEDY.CO.UK

EJ PHOTO'S
BASED IN: CAMBRIDGESHIRE
{T} 07725 694298
LIZ@EJ-PHOTOS.CO.UK
WWW.EJ-PHOTOS.CO.UK

EAMONN MCGOLDRICK PHOTOGRAPHER
BASED IN: FIFE
{T} 07810 482491
CONTACT@EAMONNMCGOLDRICK.COM
WWW.EAMONNMCGOLDRICK.COM

ELAINE TURNER PHOTOGRAPHER
BASED IN: SOMERSET
{T} 07714 762718
EAC@ELAINETURNER.CO.UK
WWW.ELAINETURNER.CO.UK

EARL PIGGOTT-SMITH PHOTOGRAPHY
BASED IN: WOLVERHAMPTON
{T} 07921 716724
EPS_PHOTO@BTINTERNET.COM
WWW.EARLPIGGOTT-SMITHPHOTOGRAPHY.CO.UK

ELIZA POWER PHOTOGRAPHY
BASED IN: LONDON
{T} 07590 370261
ELIZA.CKPOWER@GMAIL.COM
WWW.ELIZAPOWER.CO.UK

ECPHOTOGRAPHY
BASED IN: NORTHAMPTON
{T} 07956 000052
EDDPOST@GOOGLEMAIL.COM
WWW.ECPHOTOGRAPHY.CO.UK

ELLIOTT FRANKS PHOTOGRAPHY
BASED IN: LONDON
{T} 07802 537220
ELLIOTTFRANKS@GMAIL.COM
WWW.ELLIOTTFRANKS.COM

ELYSE MARKS PHOTOGRAPHY
BASED IN: LONDON
{T} 07932 038165
ELYSEMARKS@HOTMAIL.CO.UK
WWW.ELYSEMARKSPHOTOGRAPHY.COM

EMDELL PICTURES
BASED IN: LONDON
{T} 07852 363220
MIKE@EMDELL.CO.UK
WWW.EMDELL.CO.UK

EMILY BENNETT-COLES PHOTOGRAPHY
BASED IN: LONDON
{T} 02083 922351
EMILYBENNETT-COLES@HOTMAIL.CO.UK
WWW.EMILYBENNETTCOLES.COM

EOGHAN BRENNAN
BASED IN: LONDON
{T} 07598 949889
INFO@EOGHANBRENNAN.COM
WWW.EOGHANBRENNAN.COM

ERIC SCHNEIDER PHOTOGRAPHY
BASED IN: LONDON
{T} 02075 860110
ERIC@ERICSCHNEIDERPHOTOGRAPHY.COM
WWW.ERICSCHNEIDERPHOTOGRAPHY.COM

F8 GALLERY
BASED IN: YORKSHIRE
{T} 08452 570388
CLIFFORDNORTON@BTCONNECT.COM
WWW.CLIFFNORTONPHOTOGRAPHY.COM

FARROWS CREATIVE
BASED IN: BRISTOL
{T} 01275 836348
INFO@FARROWSCREATIVE.COM
WWW.FARROWSCREATIVE.COM

FATIMAH NAMDAR
BASED IN: LONDON
{T} 02083 411332
FNAMDAR@MAC.COM
WWW.FATIMAHNAMDAR.DPHOTO.COM

FAYE THOMAS
BASED IN: LONDON
{T} 07752 358106
FAYE@FAYETHOMAS.COM
WWW.FAYETHOMAS.COM

FFOTOGRAFFIAETH KEITH MORRIS PHOTOGRAPHY
BASED IN: CEREDIGION
{T} 01970 611106
KEITH@ARTSWEBWALES.COM
WWW.ARTSWEBWALES.COM

FLASHFIELDS PHOTOGRAPHY
BASED IN: LONDON
{T} 02072 632239
INFO@FLASHFIELDS.COM
WWW.FLASHFIELDS.COM

THE FOCAL SPACE PHOTOGRAPHY STUDIO
BASED IN: STEVENAGE
{T} 01438 360329
MARION@THEFOCALSPACE.COM
WWW.THEFOCALSPACE.COM

FRANK SHAPIRO PHOTOGRAPHY
BASED IN: GLASGOW
{T} 07973 106656
INFO@SHAPIROINTERNATIONAL.COM
WWW.FRANKSHAPIROPHOTOGRAPHY.COM

FRANKOWSKI PHOTOGRAPHY
BASED IN: LONDON
{T} 07939 572957
INFO@VICTORFRANKOWSKI.COM
WWW.VICTORFRANKOWSKI.COM

FRAZER ASHFORD
BASED IN: SURREY
{T} 08443 510046
FRAZER@FRAZERASHFORD.COM
WWW.CASTINGPICTURES.CO.UK

GALE PHOTOGRAPHY
BASED IN: SWINDON
{T} 01793 783859
INFO@GALEPHOTOGRAPHY.CO.UK
WWW.GALEPHOTOGRAPHY.CO.UK

GAP PHOTOGRAPHY
BASED IN: LONDON
{T} 07956 521334
GIOVANNI@GAPPHOTOGRAPHY.COM
WWW.GAPPHOTOGRAPHY.COM

GARNHAM PHOTOGRAPHY
BASED IN: LONDON
{T} 07711 941208
MARTINGARNHAM@AOL.COM
WWW.GARNHAMPHOTOGRAPHY.CO.UK

GARY BRASHIER PHOTOGRAPHY
BASED IN: MIDDLESEX
{T} 02089 430875
INFO@GARYBRASHIER.COM
WWW.GARYBRASHIER.COM

GARY DANIELL PHOTOGRAPHY
BASED IN: WEST LOTHIAN
{T} 07792 708917
GARY.DANIELL.PHOTOGRAPHY@HOTMAIL.CO.UK
WWW.GARYDANIELLPHOTOGRAPHY.ORG.UK

GARY TREADWELL
BASED IN: CORNWALL
GTREADWELL@BTINTERNET.COM
WWW.GARYTREADWELL.COM

GAVIN McQUARRIE
BASED IN: MANCHESTER
{T} 07796 556704
GAVIN0192@HOTMAIL.COM
WWW.GAVINMCQUARRIE.WEBS.COM/

GD PHOTOGRAPHY
BASED IN: ESSEX
{T} 07866 590820
GDHEADSHOTS@GOOGLEMAIL.COM
WWW.GDPHOTOGRAPHY.CO.UK

GEMMA MOUNT PHOTOGRAPHY
BASED IN: LONDON
{T} 07976 824923
GEMMA@GEMMAMOUNTPHOTOGRAPHY.COM
WWW.GEMMAMOUNTPHOTOGRAPHY.COM

GEORGEFOOTEPHOTOGRAPHY
BASED IN: BATH
{T} 07515 953217
GEORGEFOOTE@HOTMAIL.COM
WWW.GEORGEFOOTEPHOTOGRAPHY.COM

GORM SHACKELFORD
BASED IN: LONDON
{T} 07963 948915
GS@GORMSHACKELFORD.COM
WWW.GORMSHACKELFORD.CO.UK

GRAEME BRAIDWOOD PHOTOGRAPHY
BASED IN: BIRMINGHAM
{T} 07974 765644
GRAEME@GRAEMEBRAIDWOOD.COM
WWW.GRAEMEBRAIDWOOD.COM

GRAHAM BENNETT PHOTOGRAPHY
BASED IN: LONDON
{T} 02083 741697
GRAHAMDB@GMAIL.COM
WWW.GRAHAMBENNETT.BIZ

GRAHAM READING PHOTOGRAPHY
BASED IN: BUCKINGHAMSHIRE
{T} 01753 885557
GRAHAM@GRAHAMREADING.COM
WWW.GRAHAMREADING.COM

GRAHAM SILVESTER
BASED IN: KENT
{T} 02086 504492
GRAHAM@SILVESTER.CO.UK
WWW.SILVESTER.CO.UK

GRAND DESIGNER STUDIO
BASED IN: CROYDON
{T} 07921 866299
DAVID@GRANDDESIGNERSTUDIO.COM
WWW.GRANDDESIGNERSTUDIO.COM

HARRIS ASSOCIATES
BASED IN: LEEDS
{T} 01132 304411
JIM@HARRIS-ASSOCIATES.COM
WWW.HARRIS-ASSOCIATES.COM

HARRY RAFIQUE PHOTOGRAPHY
BASED IN: LONDON
{T} 02072 665398
HARRY@HR-PHOTOGRAPHER.CO.UK
WWW.HR-PHOTOGRAPHER.CO.UK

HARRY SEWELL PHOTOGRAPHY
BASED IN: LONDON
{T} 07882 475873
MAIL@HARRYSEWELL.CO.UK
WWW.HARRYSEWELL.CO.UK

HAUGAN PHOTOGRAPHY
BASED IN: MIDDLESEX
{T} 01895 677135
HARALD@HAUGANPHOTOGRAPHY.CO.UK
WWW.HAUGANPHOTOGRAPHY.CO.UK

HAYDEN PHOENIX PHOTOGRAPHER
BASED IN: LONDON
{T} 07904 572545
HAYDEN@PHOENIXIMAGES.NET
WWW.PHOENIXIMAGES.NET

HEADS UP PHOTO
BASED IN: LONDON
{T} 07966 507694
DYLAN@HEADSUPPHOTO.CO.UK
WWW.HEADSUPPHOTO.CO.UK

HEADSHOT LONDON PHOTOGRAPHY
BASED IN: LONDON
{T} 07940 444641
YANA@HEADSHOTLONDON.CO.UK
WWW.HEADSHOTLONDON.CO.UK

HEADSHOTS BY SIMON
BASED IN: LONDON
{T} 07949 660043
SIMONCARDWELL@GOOGLEMAIL.COM
WWW.HEADSHOTSBYSIMON.COM

HEADSHOTS STUDIOS
BASED IN: LONDON
{T} 07770 694686
INFO@HEADSHOTSTUDIOS.CO.UK
WWW.HEADSHOTSTUDIOS.CO.UK

HEADSHOTS UK
BASED IN: LONDON
{T} 02089 439302
SEAN@HEADSHOTSUK.CO.UK
WWW.HEADSHOTSUK.CO.UK

HEDWARD PHOTOGRAPHY
BASED IN: WAKEFIELD
{T} 07791 384178
CONTACTUS@HEDWARD.COM
WWW.HEDWARD.COM

HELEN BARTLETT PHOTOGRAPHY
BASED IN: LONDON
{T} 08456 031373
INFO@HELENBARTLETT.CO.UK
WWW.HELENBARTLETT.CO.UK

HELEN JONES PHOTOGRAPHY
BASED IN: LONDON
{T} 02085 411158
ENQUIRIES@HELENJONESPHOTOGRAPHY.CO.UK
WWW.HELENJONESPHOTOGRAPHY.CO.UK

HENBANE
BASED IN: LONDON
{T} 07999 106260
LUKE@HENBANE.NET
WWW.HENBANE.NET

HOTSHOTSPHOTOGRAPHY
BASED IN: MERSEYSIDE
{T} 01516 778393
BERNARD@HOTSHOTSPHOTOGRAPHY.CO.UK
WWW.HOTSHOTSPHOTOGRAPHY.CO.UK

HOTT AND TOTTENHAM
BASED IN: COUNTY WICKLOW
{T} 02077 299181
INFO@HOTTANDTOTTENHAM.COM
WWW.HOTTANDTOTTENHAM.COM

HUBNER PHOTOGRAPHY GLASGOW
BASED IN: GLASGOW
{T} 01415 787442
INFO@JACEKHUBNER.COM
WWW.JACEKHUBNER.COM

HUGH MACDONALD
BASED IN: NORTHAMPTONSHIRE
{T} 07773 764708
HUGHMACDONALD@BROKENPIPEFILMS.COM
WWW.BROKENPIPEFILMS.COM

HYDE END STUDIOS
BASED IN: READING
{T} 01189 885088
SIMON@HYDE-END.COM
WWW.HEDSHOTZ.CO.UK

HZV STUDIOS
BASED IN: LONDON
{T} 02083 174463
INFO@HZVSTUDIOS.COM
WWW.HZVSTUDIOS.COM

IAN M. BUTTERFIELD
BASED IN: STOCKPORT
{T} 01614 315508
IAN@2FIELDS.CO.UK
WWW.IMB.BIZ

IAN PARSFIELD PHOTOGRAPHY
BASED IN: KENT
{T} 07723 915938
IAN.PARSFIELD@GMAIL.COM
WWW.IANPARSFIELD-PHOTOGRAPHY.COM

IAN PHILLIPS-MCLAREN
BASED IN: LONDON
{T} 07889 861654
IAN@IANPHILLIPS-MCLAREN.COM
WWW.IANPHILLIPS-MCLAREN.COM

ILLUSTRASIA
BASED IN: STOCKPORT
{T} 01704 831096
INFO@ILLUSTRASIA.COM
WWW.ILLUSTRASIA.COM

IDOL IMAGES
BASED IN: DARLINGTON
{T} 01325 488385
THERESA@NEREPRESENTATION.CO.UK
WWW.IDOL-IMAGES.COM

IMAGE PHOTOGRAPHIC
BASED IN: LONDON
{T} 02076 021190
DIGITAL@IMAGEPHOTOGRAPHIC.COM
WWW.IMAGEPHOTOGRAPHIC.COM

LIGHT SPOT STUDIO
BASED IN: LONDON
{T} 02071 931893
INFO@INDRACCOLOPHOTO.CO.UK
WWW.LIGHTSPOTSTUDIO.COM

INNERLIGHT STUDIO
BASED IN: LONDON
{T} 02077 809838
INFO@STEPHANIERUSHTON.COM
WWW.STEPHANIERUSHTON.COM

ISABELLA PANATTONI
BASED IN: LONDON
{T} 07833 734117
INFO@ISABELLAPANATTONI.COM
WWW.ISABELLAPANATTONI.COM

IVES KIM
BASED IN: ESSEX
{T} 02085 020523
CONTACT@NAAMUU.CO.UK
WWW.NAAMUU.CO.UK

JACK LADENBURG
BASED IN: LONDON
{T} 07932 053743
INFO@JACKLADENBURG.CO.UK
WWW.JACKLADENBURG.CO.UK

JAMES CADMAN PHOTOGRAPHY
BASED IN: LONDON
{T} 07890 109051
JAMESCADMAN@HOTMAIL.CO.UK
WWW.JAMESCADMAN.CO.UK

JAMES DAVIES
BASED IN: SURREY
{T} 07716 515170
MAIL@JAMESDAVIESPHOTOGRAPHY.NET
WWW.JAMESDAVIESPHOTOGRAPHY.NET

JAMES PEARSON
BASED IN: GLASGOW
{T} 07932 375549
JAMESPEARSON71@MAC.COM
WWW.JAMESPEARSONPHOTOGRAPHIC.COM

JAMES WALKER PHOTOGRAPHY
BASED IN: EXETER
{T} 07977 924058
JAMES@JMWPHOTOGRAPHY.CO.UK
WWW.JMWPHOTOGRAPHY.CO.UK

JANIE RAYNE PHOTOGRAPHY
BASED IN: LONDON
{T} 07973 541780
SQP@ZOOM.CO.UK
WWW.JANIERAYNE.COM

JAYA PHOTOGRAPHY
BASED IN: LONDON
{T} 07980 649488
JAYAPHOTOGRAPHY@YMAIL.COM
WWW.JAYAPHOTOGRAPHY.CO.UK

JAZ AMPAW-FARR PHOTOGRAPHY
BASED IN: MILTON KEYNES
{T} 07941 533740
JAZ@JAZAMPAWFARR.COM
WWW.JAZAMPAWFARR.COM

JEFF MILLWARD PHOTOGRAPHY
BASED IN: WOLVERHAMPTON
{T} 01902 650595
JEFFMILLWARD@BLUEYONDER.CO.UK
WWW.JEFFMILLWARDPHOTOGRAPHY.CO.UK

JEMAA
BASED IN: LONDON
{T} 07727 715638
JEMAA@MAC.COM
WWW.JEMAA.CO.UK

JEREMY FREEDMAN
BASED IN: LONDON
{T} 07956 248662
JEREMYFREEDMAN@HOTMAIL.CO.UK
WWW.JEREMYFREEDMAN.COM

JGrayOnline.com

Based in: London
{T} 07782 113490
INFO@JGRAYONLINE.COM
WWW.JGRAYONLINE.COM

Jil Orpen Photography

Based in: London
{T} 07787 701334
JILORPEN@BTINTERNET.COM
WWW.JILORPEN.COM

Jim Lomax Photography

Based in: London
{T} 07717 605938
JIM@JIMLOMAXPHOTO.COM
WWW.JIMLOMAXPHOTO.COM

JK Photography

Based in: London
{T} 07816 825578
JKPH0T0@YAHOO.COM
WWW.JK-PHOTOGRAPHY.NET

Joe Gascoigne Photography

Based in: London
{T} 07729 979859
JOE@JOESPHOTOS.CO.UK
WWW.JOESPHOTOS.CO.UK

John Clark Photography

Based in: London
{T} 02088 544069
JOHN@JOHNCLARKPHOTOGRAPHY.COM
WWW.JOHNCLARKPHOTOGRAPHY.COM

John Cooper Photography

Based in: Glasgow
{T} 01413 347815
STUDIO@JOHNCOOPERPHOTOGRAPHY.CO.UK
WWW.JOHNCOOPERPHOTOGRAPHY.NET

John Moore Photography

Based in: London
{T} 02089 263739
JDMOORE63@AOL.COM
WWW.JOHNMOOREPHOTOGRAPHY.CO.UK

John Nichols Studio

Based in: Manchester
{T} 01614 462002
868ONLINE@GMAIL.COM
WWW.JOHNNICHOLS.CO.UK

John Tudor Photography

Based in: Leeds
{T} 07841 113574
INFO@JOHNTUDORPHOTOGRAPHY.COM
WWW.JOHNTUDORPHOTOGRAPHY.COM

John Walker Photographer

Based in: Kent
{T} 07857 159901
JOHN@JOHNWALKERPHOTOGRAPHY.CO.UK
WWW.JOHNWALKERPHOTOGRAPHY.CO.UK

Jon Campling Headshots

Based in: London
{T} 02086 798671
PHOTO@JONCAMPLING.COM
WWW.JONCAMPLINGHEADSHOTS.COM

JONATHAN BALL PHOTOGRAPHY
BASED IN: LONDON
{T} 07742 636185
INFO@JONATHANBALLPHOTOGRAPHY.COM
WWW.JONATHANBALLPHOTOGRAPHY.COM

JONATHAN BOSWORTH PHOTOGRAPHY
BASED IN: LONDON
{T} 07739 738570
JONBOSWORTH@HOTMAIL.CO.UK
WWW.JONATHANBOSWORTH.CO.UK

JONNY DONOVAN PHOTOGRAPHY
BASED IN: LONDON
{T} 07702 785004
JONNYDONOVAN@GMAIL.COM
WWW.JONNYDONOVAN.COM

JOSEPH STORY
BASED IN: LONDON
{T} 07957 691692
JOSEPH@JOSEPHSINCLAIR.COM
WWW.JOSEPHSINCLAIR.COM

JOSEPH SINCLAIR
BASED IN: MANCHESTER
{T} 07515 474851
JOSEPHSTORYIMAGES@GOOGLEMAIL.COM
WWW.JSTORYPHOTOGRAPHY.COM

JOSHUA MILLAIS PHOTOGRAPHY
BASED IN: LONDON
{T} 02077 923218
EMAIL@JOSHUAMILLAIS.COM
WWW.JOSHUAMILLAIS.COM

JOTH SHAKERLEY
BASED IN: LONDON
{T} 02089 645823
JOTHSHAKERLEY@YAHOO.CO.UK
WWW.JOTH SHAKERLEY.COM

JULES LAWRENCE PHOTOGRAPHY
BASED IN: LONDON
{T} 07939 157142
JULES@JULESLAWRENCE.CO.UK
WWW.JULESLAWRENCE.CO.UK

JULIA BURSTEIN PHOTOGRAPHY
BASED IN: LONDON
{T} 02072 720738
PHOTOGRAPHY@JULIABURSTEIN.COM
WWW.JULIABURSTEIN.COM

JULIA WATES PHOTOGRAPHY
BASED IN: LONDON
{T} 02087 414667
JULIAWATES@HOTMAIL.COM
WWW.JULIA-WATESPHOTOGRAPHY.COM

JULIE PHILPOT PHOTOGRAPHY
BASED IN: ESSEX
{T} 07889 978920
PHILPOTJULIE@HOTMAIL.COM
WWW.JULIEPHILPOTPHOTOGRAPHY.CO.UK

JUSTACTORS.CO.UK
BASED IN: ESSEX
CASTINGCALLPRO@JUSTACTORS.CO.UK
WWW.JUSTACTORS.CO.UK

KAIZ AGENCY
BASED IN: LONDON
{T} 07739 562713
INFO@KAIZAGENCY.COM
WWW.KAIZAGENCY.COM

KARCZMARZ STUDIOS
BASED IN: LONDON
{T} 07932 582544
KARCZMARZ.STUDIOS@GOOGLEMAIL.COM
WWW.NEXTCAT.COM/STAN_KARCZMARZ

KARLA GOWLETT
BASED IN: LONDON
{T} 07941 871271
INFO@KARLAGOWLETT.CO.UK
WWW.PHOTOPERSPECTIVE.CO.UK

KASTAKEPHOTO
BASED IN: LONDON
{T} 07966 412908
PHOTO@KAS.ME.UK
WWW.KAS.ME.UK

KATHERINE JAMES PHOTOGRAPHY
BASED IN: LONDON
KATHERINE.JAMES28@YAHOO.CO.UK
WWW.KATHERINE-JAMES.COM

KATHRYNDAISY PHOTOGRAPHY
BASED IN: LONDON
{T} 07732 222876
KATHRYNDAISY@YAHOO.CO.UK
WWW.KATHRYNDAISYPHOTOGRAPHY.COM

KERR-CLICK.COM
BASED IN: LONDON
{T} 07931 537363
ANGELAEDWARDS1@ME.COM
WWW.KERR-CLICK.COM

KERRY SKINNER PHOTOGRAPHY
BASED IN: LONDON
{T} 02087 729168
KERRYSKINNER@BTINTERNET.COM
WWW.KERRYSKINNERPHOTOGRAPHY.CO.UK

KEVIN SHIPLEY PHOTOGRAPHIC
BASED IN: BOLTON
{T} 01204 492039
KEVIN.SHIPLEY@HOMECALL.CO.UK
WWW.PHOTOBOXGALLERY.COM/2094

KIM SHEARD PHOTOGRAPHY
BASED IN: LONDON
{T} 07817 769666
CONTACT@KIMSHEARDPHOTOGRAPHY.COM
WWW.KIMSHEARDPHOTOGRAPHY.COM

KIM THORN PHOTOGRAPHY
BASED IN: HERTFORDSHIRE
{T} 01442 262820
ENQUIRIES@KIMTHORNPHOTOGRAPHY.CO.UK
WWW.KIMTHORNPHOTOGRAPHY.CO.UK

KIRSTEN MCTERNAN PHOTOGRAPHY & DESIGN
BASED IN: CARDIFF
{T} 07791 524551
KIRSTEN@KIRSTENMCTERNAN.CO.UK
WWW.KIRSTENMCTERNAN.CO.UK

KIRRIL PHOTOGRAPHY
BASED IN: LONDON
{T} 0207 682 1655
KIRILL_UK@HOTMAIL.COM
WWW.KIRILL.CO.UK

KOENIGMA
BASED IN: DORSET
{T} 07919 140818
IAN@KOENIGMA.COM
WWW.KOENIGMA.COM

KSENIA KAMOTSKAIA PHOTOGRAPHY
BASED IN: GLASGOW
{T} 07751 233544
KKAMOTSKAIA@HOTMAIL.COM
WWW.KSENIAKAMOTSKAIAPHOTOGRAPHY.COM

LATTE PHOTOGRAPHY
BASED IN: GLAMORGAN
{T} 01656 743007
CHRIS.BBBB@TESCO.NET
WWW.LATTEPHOTOGRAPHY.IFP3.COM

LEES-IMAGES
BASED IN: BRIGHTON
{T} 02030 518247
LEE@LEES-IMAGES.CO.UK
WWW.LEES-IMAGES.CO.UK

LEGEND PHOTOGRAPHY
BASED IN: EAST SUSSEX
{T} 01424 430055
OLIVER@LEGEND-PHOTOGRAPHY.COM
WWW.LEGEND-PHOTOGRAPHY.COM

LEMBERTH STUDIO™
BASED IN: LONDON
{T} 07855 488727
LEMBERTH@ME.COM
WWW.LEMBERTH.CO.UK

LENKA JONES PHOTOGRAPHY
BASED IN: WINDSOR
{T} 07921 182055
LENKI13@YAHOO.CO.UK
WWW.LENKAJONESPHOTOGRAPHY.COM

LESAUVAGE
BASED IN: LONDON
{T} 07748 651830
LESAUVAGE@MAC.COM
WWW.LESAUVAGEPHOTGRAPHER.COM

THE LIGHT ROOMS
BASED IN: LONDON
{T} 0207 4396777
ENQUIRIES@THELIGHTROOMS.COM
WWW.THELIGHTROOMS.COM

THE LIGHT STUDIOS
BASED IN: LONDON
{T} 02076 106036
INFO@LIGHTSTUDIOS.NET
WWW.LIGHTSTUDIOS.ORG

LINSEY O'NEILL DESIGN
BASED IN: DORSET
{T} 01202 680312
LINSEY@LINSEY-ONEILL-DESIGN.CO.UK
WWW.LINSEY-ONEILL-DESIGN.CO.UK

LintonLaidley Photograher
Based in: Sussex
{T} 07930 344041
LINTONS@HOTMAIL.CO.UK
WWW.LINTONLAIDLEY.CO.UK

London Headshot
Based in: London
{T} 02076 098366
HENRY@LONDON-HEADSHOT.CO.UK
WWW.LONDON-HEADSHOT.CO.UK

London Headshot Photography
Based in: London
{T} 02083 493632
LYNNHERRICK@GMAIL.COM
WWW.HEADSHOTSLONDON.CO.UK

London Photographer
Based in: London
{T} 07834 524525
INFO@MARGARETYESCOMBE.COM
WWW.MARGARETYESCOMBE.COM

London Photographers
Based in: London
{T} 02081 441985
HELLO@THELONDONPHOTOGRAPHERS.COM
WWW.THELONDONPHOTOGRAPHERS.COM

London Photography Studio
Based in: London
{T} 07942 022003
AGATA.PREYSS@GMAIL.COM
WWW.LONDONPHOTOGRAPHYSTUDIO.COM

Lost Art Logic
Based in: Birmingham
{T} 01214 712991
ANDREWBAINBRIDGE@LOSTARTLOGIC.CO.UK
WWW.MYSPACE.COM/LOSTARTLOGICLTD

Louise O'Gorman Photography
Based in: London
INFO@LOUISEOGORMAN.COM
WWW.LOUISEOGORMAN.COM

Lukas Photography
Based in: Worthing
{T} 01903 521509
LUKASPHOTOGRAPHIC@HOTMAIL.COM
MICBMANAGEMENT.CO.UK

Luke de Woolfson Photography
Based in: London
{T} 07968 761232
PHOTOGRAPHY@LUKEDEWOOLFSON.COM
WWW.LUKEDEWOOLFSON.COM

Luke Varley / Photo
Based in: London
{T} 07711 183631
LUKE@LUKEVARLEY.COM
WWW.LUKEVARLEY.COM

LWE
Based in: London
{T} 07900 073089
INFO@LWELEPHANT.CO.UK
WWW.LWELEPHANT.CO.UK/PHOTOGRAPHY

M.A.D. PHOTOGRAPHY
BASED IN: LONDON
{T} 02083 634182
MAD.PHOTO@ONETEL.NET
WWW.MAD-PHOTOGRAPHY.CO.UK

MAGIC SNAPS
BASED IN: ESSEX
{T} 01708 732298
MAGICSNAPS@GOOGLEMAIL.COM
WWW.MAGICSNAPS.CO.UK

MAGNUS HASTINGS
BASED IN: LONDON
{T} 07905 304705
MAGNUS@MAGNUSHASTINGS.CO.UK
WWW.MAGNUSHASTINGS.CO.UK

MARC BROUSSELY
BASED IN: LONDON
{T} 07738 920225
MARC@MARCBROUSSELY.COM
WWW.MARCBROUSSELY.COM

MARC HANKINS PHOTOGRAPHIC
BASED IN: SURREY
{T} 07809 433555
MARC@MARCHANKINS.COM
WWW.MARCHANKINS.COM

MARCOS BEVILACQUA PHOTOGRAPHY
BASED IN: LONDON
{T} 02076 830954
INFO@MARCOS-BOOK.COM
WWW.MARCOS-BOOK.COM

MARCUS ROSS
BASED IN: LONDON
{T} 07747 758877
MAIL@MARCUSROSS.NET
WWW.MARCUSROSS.NET

MARK ARMITAGE PHOTOGRAPHY
BASED IN: MANCHESTER
{T} 07867 544282
ARMITAGEPORTRAITURE@HOTMAIL.CO.UK
WWW.ARMITAGEPORTRAITURE.MOONFRUIT.COM

MARK BARNFIELD
BASED IN: LONDON
{T} 02072 725040
MARK@MARKBARNFIELD.NET
WWW.MARKBARNFIELD.NET

MARK BLOWER PHOTOGRAPHY
BASED IN: LONDON
{T} 07958 463474
INFO@MARKBLOWER.COM
WWW.MARKBLOWER.COM

MARK BROME PHOTOGRAPHER
BASED IN: OXFORDSHIRE
{T} 01235 519202
INFO@MARKBROME.COM
WWW.MARKBROME.COM

MARK BYRNE PHOTOGRAPHER
BASED IN: MANCHESTER
{T} 01204 651947
MARK@MARKBYRNE.CO.UK
WWW.MARKBYRNE.CO.UK

MARK EDMONDSON - PHOTOGRAPHIC ARTIST
BASED IN: PRESTON
{T} 01772 465258
MARK@MEPHOTOGRAPHY.CO.UK
WWW.NORTHWESTGLAMOUR.CO.UK

MARK WHITFIELD PHOTOGRAPHY
BASED IN: LONDON
{T} 07889 581061
MARK@MARKWHITFIELDPHOTOGRAPHY.COM
WWW.MARKWHITFIELDPHOTOGRAPHY.COM

MARTIN COYNE PHOTOGRAPHY
BASED IN: BOURNEMOUTH
{T} 07788 788616
MARTIN@MARTINCOYNE.COM
WWW.MARTINCOYNE.COM

MARTIN SAINT PHOTOGRAPHY
BASED IN: LONDON
{T} 02085 033159
INFO@MARTINSAINT.COM
WWW.MARTINSAINT.COM

MATT JAMIE PHOTOGRAPHY
BASED IN: LONDON
{T} 07976 890643
PHOTOS@MATTJAMIE.CO.UK
WWW.MATTJAMIE.CO.UK/PORTRAITS

MATT STEDEFORD PHOTOGRAPHY
BASED IN: LONDON
{T} 07793 741604
MATTSTEDEFORD@GMAIL.COM
WWW.STEDEFORD.COM

MATTHEW NORTH
BASED IN: CARDIFF/LONDON
{T} 07973 354306
MATT.NORTH@TALK21.COM
WWW.MATTHEWNORTH.CO.UK

MATTHEW SEED PHOTOGRAPHY
BASED IN: LONDON
{T} 08001 695630
MATTHEW@MSPSTUDIO.CO.UK
WWW.MSPSTUDIO.CO.UK

MAXINE EVANS - PHOTOS FOR ACTORS
BASED IN: LONDON
{T} 07966 130426
MAXINEVANS@AOL.COM
WWW.PHOTOSFORACTORS.CO.UK

MDO STUDIO
BASED IN: SURREY
{T} 07968 245901
HURSTMEREC@HOTMAIL.COM
WWW.MODELLING.ORG.UK

MEONSHORE STUDIOS LTD
BASED IN: HAMPSHIRE
{T} 01329 310314
MIKEFRENCH@MEONSHORESTUDIOS.CO.UK
WWW.MEONSHORECOMMERCIAL.CO.UK

MERE WORDS PHOTOGRAPHY
BASED IN: KENT
{T} 01322 555723
MARC@MEREWORDS.CO.UK
WWW.MEREWORDS.CO.UK

MICHAEL BRYDON PHOTOGRAPHY
BASED IN: LONDON
{T} 07875 600031
INFO@MICHAELBRYDON.CO.UK
WWW.MICHAELBRYDON.CO.UK

MICHAEL HEDGE
BASED IN: LONDON
{T} 07725 565977
MICHAEL@MICHAELHEDGE.CO.UK
WWW.MICHAELHEDGE.CO.UK

MICHAEL HOLMAN PHOTOGRAPHY
BASED IN: SOMERSET
{T} 07803 906663
MICHAEL@MICHAELHOLMAN.NET
WWW.MICHAELHOLMAN.NET

MICHAEL POLLARD
BASED IN: NORTH WEST ENGLAND
{T} 01614 567470
INFO@MICHAELPOLLARD.CO.UK
WWW.MICHAELPOLLARD.CO.UK

MICHAEL WHARLEY PHOTOGRAPHY
BASED IN: LONDON
{T} 07961 068759
MICHAELWHARLEY@GOOGLEMAIL.COM
WWW.MICHAELWHARLEY.CO.UK

MICHAELWHEELERPHOTO.COM
BASED IN: LONDON
{T} 07932 756244
INFO@MICHAELWHEELERPHOTO.COM
WWW.MICHAELWHEELERPHOTO.COM

MIKE TSANG PHOTOGRAPHY
BASED IN: LONDON
{T} 07803 198381
INFO@MIKETSANGPHOTOGRAPHY.COM
WWW.MIKETSANGPHOTOGRAPHY.COM

MILAEON LTD
BASED IN: LONDON
{T} 02089 933903
INFO@MILAEON.CO.UK
WWW.MILAEON.CO.UK

MINOT STUDIOS
BASED IN: LONDON
{T} 02089 862743
INFO@STUDIOMINOT.COM
WWW.STUDIOMINOT.COM

MISHA VON BENNIGSEN PHOTOGRAPHY
BASED IN: LONDON
{T} 02074 338080
MISHA@MISHAPHOTOGRAPHY.CO.UK
WWW.MISHAPHOTOGRAPHY.CO.UK

MISSION PHOTOGRAPHIC
BASED IN: CARDIFF
{T} 07816 857450
MEI@MISSIONPHOTOGRAPHIC.COM
WWW.MISSIONPHOTOGRAPHIC.COM

MO CARRIM PHOTOGRAPHY (NOTTING HILL)
BASED IN: LONDON
{T} 02074 602183
MOCARRIM@YAHOO.CO.UK
WWW.MYSPACE.COM/MOCARRIM

MotionAndStills.com
Based in: Glasgow
{T} 01415 761891
stephen@motionandstills.com
www.MotionAndStills.com

My Headshots
Based in: Cambridgeshire
{T} 01480 301482
martyn@myheadshots.co.uk
www.MyHeadshots.co.uk

Nando Machado Photography
Based in: London
{T} 07898 772790
mail@nandophoto.com
www.nandophoto.com

Natalie J Watts Photography
Based in: London
{T} 07967 361365
nataliejwatts@hotmail.com
www.nataliejwatts.com

Natalie Muallem Photographer
Based in: London
{T} 07957 631043
nataliemuallem@hotmail.com
www.nataliemuallem.com

Natasha Merchant
Based in: London
{T} 02086 535399
natashamerchant@mac.com
www.natashamerchant.com

Neal Criscuolo Photography
Based in: London
{T} 02088 191222
info@nealcriscuolo.com
www.nealcriscuolo.com

Neil Fortescue
Based in: Essex
{T} 07791 520724
neil@neilfortescue.com
www.neilfortescue.com

Neil Waterson Photography
Based in: London
{T} 02077 046267
info@neilwaterson.com
www.neilwaterson.com

Neolestat.com
Based in: Cornwall
{T} 07795 262665
andy@neolestat.com
www.neolestat.com

Nicholas Dawkes Photography
Based in: London
{T} 07787 111997
nicholasdawkes@yahoo.co.uk
www.nicholasdawkesphotography.co.uk

Nick Gregan Photography
Based in: London
{T} 02085 333003
info@nickgregan.com
www.nickgregan.com

NKPHOTOGRAPHER
BASED IN: SURREY
{T} 07782 202072
NINA@NKPHOTOGRAPHER.COM
WWW.NKPHOTOGRAPHER.COM

NODACHI DESIGN
BASED IN: LONDON
{T} 07886 329313
AJAY@NODACHI.CO.UK
WWW.NODACHI.CO.UK

NOEL SHELLEY PHOTOGRAPHY
BASED IN: LONDON
{T} 07762 661662
NOELSHELLEY@HOTMAIL.COM
WWW.NOELSHELLEY.COM

NORWICH PHOTO
BASED IN: NORWICH
{T} 07798 651441
ANDREW@NORWICHPHOTO.CO.UK
WWW.NORWICHPHOTO.CO.UK

OLYDEN JOHNSON PHOTOGRAPHY
BASED IN: MIDDLESEX
{T} 02089 323880
OJ@OLYDEN.COM
WWW.OLYDEN.COM

PAIGE BIRNIE PHOTOGRAPHY
BASED IN: LONDON
{T} 07531 721546
PAIGE@PAIGEBIRNIE.COM
WWW.PAIGEBERNIE.COM

PANDA STUDIO
BASED IN: LONDON
{T} 02089 469191
ANDREI@PANDASTUDIO.CO.UK
WWW.PANDASTUDIO.CO.UK

PANK SETHI PHOTOGRAPHY
BASED IN: LONDON
{T} 07919 436836
PANKSETHI@YAHOO.COM
WWW.PANKSETHI-PHOTOGRAPHY.CO.UK

PASCAL MOLLIERE
BASED IN: LONDON
{T} 07713 242948
PASCAL@PASCALPHOTO.CO.UK
WWW.PASCALPHOTO.CO.UK

PATRICK BOWYER
BASED IN: SURREY
{T} 07907 775099
PATRICKBOWYER@GMAIL.COM
WWW.PATRICKBOWYER.COM

PAUL BARRASS PHOTOGRAPHY
BASED IN: LONDON
{T} 02085 331492
PAUL@PAULBARRASS.CO.UK
WWW.PAULBARRASS.CO.UK

PAUL CABLE PHOTOGRAPHY & DESIGN
BASED IN: ESSEX
{T} 07958 932764
INFO@PAULCABLE.COM
WWW.PAULCABLE.COM

PAUL JONES PHOTOGRAPHY
BASED IN: MANCHESTER
{T} 01617 379163
INFO@PAULJONES-PHOTOGRAPHER.COM
WWW.PAULJONES-PHOTOGRAPHER.COM

PAUL SPENCER CLAMP PHOTOGRAPHY
BASED IN: SUSSEX
{T} 01273 323782
PAULSPENCERCLAMP@YAHOO.CO.UK
WWW.PSCPHOT.COM

PAUL STONE PHOTOGRAPHY
BASED IN: ESSEX
{T} 07504 270896
PAULJAMESHENRY@MSN.COM
WWW.PAULSTONEPHOTOGRAPHY.COM

PBG-PORTRAITS
BASED IN: LONDON
{T} 07961 453109
GAZ@PBG-PORTRAITS.COM
WWW.PBG-PORTRAITS.COM

PEPE ESCUREDO PHOTOGRAPHY
BASED IN: LONDON
{T} 07956 175863
INFO@TALENTSHOTS.CO.UK
WWW.TALENTSHOTS.CO.UK/HEADSHOTS

THE PERFORMING ARTS STUDIO
BASED IN: LONDON
{T} 02075 661246
INFO@PERFORMINGARTSSTUDIO.CO.UK
WWW.PERFORMINGARTSSTUDIO.CO.UK

PETE BARTLETT PHOTOGRAPHY
BASED IN: LONDON
{T} 07971 653994
INFO@PETEBARTLETT.COM
WWW.PETEBARTLETTHEADSHOTS.CO.UK

PETE LE MAY
BASED IN: LONDON
{T} 07703 649246
PETE@PETELEMAY.CO.UK
WWW.PETELEMAY.CO.UK

PETER BOYD PHOTOGRAPHY
BASED IN: WEST YORKSHIRE
{T} 07793 200186
INFO@PBPHOTO.CO.UK
WWW.PBPHOTO.CO.UK

PETER HALL PHOTOGRAPHY
BASED IN: LONDON
{T} 0208 981 2822
WWW.THEREALPETERHALL.COM

PETER SIMPKIN
BASED IN: LONDON
{T} 02083 642634
PETERSIMPKIN@AOL.COM
WWW.PETERSIMPKIN.CO.UK

PETER TEIGEN PHOTOGRAPHY
BASED IN: LONDON
{T} 07939 224463
PETERTEIGEN@YAHOO.CO.UK
WWW.PETERTEIGEN.COM

PHIL CROW
BASED IN: LINCOLN
{T} 07787 155852
ENQUIRY@PHILCROW.COM
WWW.PHILCROW.COM

PHILIP HUNTON PHOTOGRAPHY
BASED IN: NEWCASTLE UPON TYNE
{T} 01912 361017
INFO@PHILIPHUNTON.CO.UK
WWW.PHILIPHUNTON.CO.UK

PHILIP RAYMOND PHOTOGRAPHY
BASED IN: LONDON
{T} 07966 687821
PHILSINBOX@HOTMAIL.CO.UK
WWW.PHILIPRAYMONDPHOTOGRAPHY.COM

PHILIP WADE PHOTOGRAPHY
BASED IN: LONDON
{T} 02072 263088
PIX@PHILIPWADE.COM
WWW.PHILIPWADE.COM

PHILIPPA STRANDBERG PHOTOGRAPHY
BASED IN: SUSSEX
{T} 02086 897405
INFO@PHILIPPASTRANDBERG.COM
WWW.PHILIPPASTRANDBERG.COM

PHOTOE
BASED IN: LONDON
{T} 02083 483149
ENQUIRY@PHOTOE.CO.UK
WWW.PHOTOE.CO.UK

PHOTOEXPOSURE
BASED IN: BERKSHIRE
INFO@PHOTOEXPOSURE.CO.UK
WWW.PHOTOEXPOSURE.CO.UK

PHOTOGRAPHSOF.COM
BASED IN: SWANSEA
{T} 07554 011410
LIAM@PHOTOGRAPHSOF.COM
WWW.PHOTOGRAPHSOF.COM

PHOTOGRAPHY BY PAUL AND JACS
BASED IN: CARDIFF
{T} 02920 565076
PAUL@PHOTOGRAPHYBYPAULANDJACS.COM
WWW.PHOTOGRAPHYBYPAULANDJACS.COM

THE PHOTO STAR
BASED IN: LEICESTERSHIRE
{T} 01455 230116
WOWPHOTOGRAPHY@BTINTERNET.COM
WWW.THEPHOTOSTAR.COM

PICTURE MEDIA
BASED IN: LONDON
{T} 07973 555111
MAX@PICTUREMEDIA.CO.UK
WWW.PICTUREMEDIA.CO.UK

PICTURES INC LTD
BASED IN: MIDDLESEX
{T} 07810 888373
PAUL@PICTURESINC.CO.UK
WWW.PICTURESINC.CO.UK/ACTORS

PICTURESBYBISH
BASED IN: NEWCASTLE UPON TYNE
{T} 07861 667151
INFO@PICTURESBYBISH.COM
WWW.PICTURESBYBISH.COM

PIERRE MARCAR
BASED IN: SURREY
{T} 07956 485584
SHOOTME@PIERREMARCARPEOPLE.COM
WWW.PIERREMARCARPEOPLE.COM

PIOTR KOWALIK PHOTOGRAPHY
BASED IN: LONDON
{T} 07946 323631
KPIOTR@BTINTERNET.COM
WWW.PIOTRKOWALIK.CO.UK

PIXELS
BASED IN: DONCASTER
{T} 07876 792017
DAWN@PIXELSIMAGES.CO.UK
WWW.PIXELSIMAGES.CO.UK

PRESS PHOTOGRAPHERS
BASED IN: STRATFORD ON AVON
{T} 08707 773037
INFO@PRESSPHOTOGRAPHERS.CO.UK
WWW.PRESSPHOTOGRAPHERS.CO.UK

PROFILE PHOTOGRAPHY
BASED IN: LONDON
{T} 07971 431798
KATIEROLLETT@YAHOO.CO.UK
WWW.PROFILE-LONDON.COM

RACHEL LYNCH PHOTOGRAPHY
BASED IN: WREXHAM
{T} 07835 129043
INFO@RACHELLYNCHPHOTOGRAPHY.COM
WWW.RACHELLYNCHPHOTOGRAPHY.COM

REMY HUNTER PHOTOGRAPHY
BASED IN: LONDON
{T} 02074 318055
REMY_HUNTER@HOTMAIL.COM
WWW.REMYHUNTER.CO.UK

RENATA AIELLO PHOTOGRAPHY
BASED IN: LONDON
{T} 07527 028131
RENATA@RENATAAIELLO.COM
WWW.ACTORSPHOTOGRAPHY.CO.UK

RETRO REELS
BASED IN: LONDON
{T} 07896 299932
MAIL@RETROREELS.CO.UK
WWW.RETROREELS.CO.UK

RETRORUBBER PHOTOGRAPHY
BASED IN: LONDON
{T} 07530 217836
BRIAN@RETRORUBBER.NET
WWW.RETRORUBBER.NET

RIC BACON PHOTOGRAPHY
BASED IN: LONDON
{T} 07970 970799
BAKES69@HOTMAIL.COM
WWW.RICBACON.CO.UK

RICH HENDRY PHOTOGRAPHY
BASED IN: LONDON
{T} 07801 567215
RICH@RICHHENDRY.COM
WWW.RICHHENDRY.COM

RICHARD CAMPBELL PHOTOGRAPHY
BASED IN: GLASGOW
{T} 01412 374066
STUDIO@RICHARDCAMPBELL.CO.UK
WWW.RICHARDCAMPBELL.CO.UK

RICHARD DUTKOWSKI FBIPP FMPA
BASED IN: CARDIFF
{T} 02920 621665
ENQUIRIES@DUTKOWSKI.CO.UK
WWW.DUTKOWSKI.CO.UK

RICHARD GREBBY
BASED IN: KENT
{T} 07850 304539
RICHARD@RICHARDGREBBY.CO.UK
WWW.RICHARDGREBBY.CO.UK

RICHARD PRICE PHOTOGRAPHY
BASED IN: MANCHESTER
{T} 07803 177715
INFO@RICHARDPRICEPHOTOGRAPHY.CO.UK
WWW.RICHARDPRICEPHOTOGRAPHY.CO.UK

RICHARD UNGER PHOTOGRAPHY
BASED IN: HERTFORDSHIRE
{T} 01462 892381
RICHARD@RICHARDUNGER.COM
WWW.RICHARDUNGER.COM

RIVER STUDIO
BASED IN: BIRMINGHAM
{T} 01216 244777
INFO@RIVERSTUDIO.CO.UK
WWW.RICHARDBATTYE.COM

ROB BOOKER PHOTOGRAPHY
BASED IN: YORKSHIRE
{T} 01132 702440
CONTACT@ROBBOOKER.CO.UK
WWW.ROBBOOKER.CO.UK

ROB JEWELL PHOTOGRAPHY
BASED IN: CORNWALL
{T} 01736 751781
ROB@RJPHOTO.CO.UK
WWW.RJPHOTO.CO.UK

ROB PERCY PHOTOGRAPHY
BASED IN: MAIDENHEAD
{T} 01628 684659
INFO@ROBPERCY.CO.UK
WWW.ROBPERCY.CO.UK

ROB SPUFFARD PHOTOGRAPHY
BASED IN: STAFFORDSHIRE
{T} 07535 014914
RS_PHOTOGRAPHY@HOTMAIL.CO.UK
WWW.ROB-SPUFFARD.COM

ROBERT GOOCH
BASED IN: KENT
{T} 07976 965577
INFO@ROBERTGOOCH.COM
WWW.ROBERTGOOCH.COM

ROBERT JAMES TAYLOR PHOTOGRAPHY
BASED IN: MANCHESTER
{T} 01614 081239
RJTAYLOR@RJTMAIL.COM
WWW.RJTHEADSHOTS.COM

ROBERT OTTENBURGER PHOTOGRAPHY
BASED IN: LONDON
{T} 07903 950503
OTTENBURGER@YAHOO.CO.UK
WWW.OTTENBURGER.COM

ROBERT WORKMAN PHOTOGRAPHER LTD
BASED IN: LONDON
{T} 02073 855442
BOB@ROBERTWORKMAN.DEMON.CO.UK
WWW.ROBERTWORKMAN.DEMON.CO.UK

ROBIN SAVAGE PHOTOGRAPHY
BASED IN: LONDON
{T} 07901 927597
CONTACT@ROBINSAVAGE.CO.UK
WWW.ROBINSAVAGE.CO.UK

ROCKWELL MEDIA UK
BASED IN: DUNDEE
{T} 01382 434711
ROCKWELLCM@BLUEYONDER.CO.UK
WWW.ROCKWELLMEDIA.CO.UK

ROCCO REDONDO
BASED IN: LONDON
{T} 07770 694686
WWW.ROCCOREDONDO.COM

RODOGRAPHY
BASED IN: LONDON
{T} 07717 723134
RODERICKBB@RODOGRAPHY.COM
WWW.RODOGRAPHY.COM

ROKAS DARULIS PHOTOGRAPHY
BASED IN: LONDON
{T} 07904 925995
PHOTO@ROKASDARULIS.CO.UK
WWW.ROKASDARULIS.CO.UK

ROLFE MARKHAM PHOTOGRAPHY
BASED IN: LONDON
{T} 02087 881176
ROLFE@ROLFEMARKHAM.CO.UK
WWW.ROLFEMARKHAM.CO.UK

ROMAIN FORQUY
BASED IN: LONDON
{T} 07968 632029
INFO@PHOTOCABIN.CO.UK
WWW.PHOTOCABIN.CO.UK

RORY BUCKLAND PHOTOGRAPHER
BASED IN: BIRMINGHAM
{T} 07887 897749
INFO@RORYBUCKLAND.COM
WWW.RORYBUCKLAND.COM

ROSIE STILL
BASED IN: LONDON
{T} 02088 576920
ROSIE@ROSIESTILLPHOTOGRAPHY.COM
WWW.ROSIESTILLPHOTOGRAPHY.COM

ROSS AITKEN PHOTOGRAPHY
BASED IN: EDINBURGH
{T} 07816 418236
ROSSJ8KEN@GMAIL.COM
WWW.ROSS-AITKEN.COM

ROSY CLARKE PHOTOGRAPHER
BASED IN: LONDON
{T} 07531 171074
MEERHAY@AOL.COM
WWW.ROSYCLARKEPHOTOGRAPHER.COM

ROUND ISLAND
BASED IN: LONDON
{T} 07703 279546
PHOTOS@ROUNDISLAND.NET
WWW.ROUNDISLAND.NET/PHOTOGRAPHY

RUTH CRAFER PHOTOGRAPHER
BASED IN: LONDON
{T} 07974 088460
RUTH.CRAFER@MAC.COM
WWW.RUTHCRAFER.CO.UK

RUTH MULHOLLAND PHOTOGRAPHY
BASED IN: LONDON
{T} 07939 516987
RUTH@RUTHMULHOLLAND.COM
WWW.RUTHMULHOLLAND.COM

SAM CLARK PHOTOGRAPHY
BASED IN: DEVON
{T} 01566 783233
SAM@FARLAP.CO.UK
WWW.SAMCLARKPHOTOGRAPHY.COM

SAM K MASSEY PHOTOGRAPHY
BASED IN: LONDON
{T} 07843 246236
SAMKMASSEY@HOTMAIL.COM
WWW.SAMKMASSEY.COM

SANDI HODKINSON PHOTOGRAPHY
BASED IN: MANCHESTER
{T} 0161 865 7930
SANDIHODKINSON@YAHOO.CO.UK
WWW.SANDIHODKINSON.CO.UK

SARA LEIGH LEWIS PHOTOGRAPHY
BASED IN: LONDON
{T} 02072 529324
SARA@SARALEIGHLEWIS.CO.UK
WWW.SARALEIGHLEWIS.CO.UK

SARAH ROESINK PHOTOGRAPHY
BASED IN: LONDON
{T} 07775 730298
SARAH.ROESINK@GMX.DE
WWW.SARAHROESINK.NET

SAREL JANSEN
BASED IN: LONDON
{T} 08004 488465
INFO@SARELJANSEN.COM
WWW.SARELJANSEN.COM

SASHACD
BASED IN: LONDON
{T} 07973 883687
SASHACD@OREV.CO.UK
WWW.SASHACD.CO.UK

SCALLYWAGS / LEON PHOTOGRAPHY
BASED IN: ESSEX
{T} 02085 539999
PHILIP@SCALLYWAGS.CO.UK
WWW.SCALLYWAGS.CO.UK

SCHOOL OF ART
BASED IN: LONDON
{T} 02077 939315
AFRANCK@BTINTERNET.COM
WWW.ALEXFRANCK.COM

SCORCHING IMAGE PHOTOGRAPHY
BASED IN: KENT
{T} 08704 321338
DAVE.WISE@SCORCHINGIMAGE.COM
WWW.SCORCHINGIMAGE.COM

SCOTT AND BARNES PHOTOGRAPHY
BASED IN: LONDON
{T} 08006 124453
ONEBLAKESCOTT@YAHOO.CO.UK
WWW.SCOTTANDBARNESPHOTOGRAPHY.COM

SHAMBHALA
BASED IN: LONDON
{T} 07930 101299
SHAMBHALA.PHOTO@GMAIL.COM
WWW.PHOTO.NET/PHOTOS/SHAMBHALA

SHAMEFUL PHOTOGRAPHIC
BASED IN: LONDON
{T} 02086 789591
PADDY@SHAMEFULPHOTOGRAPHIC.COM
WWW.SHAMEFULPHOTOGRAPHIC.COM

SHANA WILSON PHOTOGRAPHY
BASED IN: SUFFOLK
{T} 07821 961818
WILSON_147@MSN.COM
WWW.SWPONLINE.WEBS.COM

SHEILA BURNETT
BASED IN: LONDON
{T} 02072 893058
SHEILAB33@NTLWORLD.COM
WWW.SHEILABURNETT-PHOTOGRAPHY.COM

SHERYL TAIT PHOTOGRAPHY
BASED IN: LONDON
{T} 07977 487627
SHERYLTAIT@GOOGLEMAIL.COM
WWW.SHERYLTAIT.COM

SHOOT THE MOON PHOTOGRAPHY
BASED IN: MANCHESTER
{T} 01612 057417
ELAINE@SHOOT-THE-MOON.CO.UK
WWW.STMPHOTOGRAPHY.CO.UK

SHOOTING SUZIE PHOTOGRAPHY
BASED IN: KENT
{T} 07739 937367
KELLY@SHOOTINGSUZIE.COM
WWW.SHOOTINGSUZIE.COM

SHOT BY THE SHERIFF PHOTOGRAPHY
BASED IN: LONDON
{T} 08000 377703
PHOTOS@SHOTBYTHESHERIFF.CO.UK
WWW.SHOTBYTHESHERIFF.CO.UK

ShotID
Based in: Cheshire
{T} 01613 550869
JAY@SHOTID.CO.UK
WWW.SHOTID.CO.UK

Simon Annand
Based in: London
{T} 02072 416725
SIMONANNAND@BLUEYONDER.CO.UK
WWW.SIMONANNANDHEADSHOTS.CO.UK

Simon Goodwin
Based in: London
{T} 07760 252772
SIMON.GOODWIN@HOTMAIL.COM
WWW.SIMONGOODWIN.COM

Simon Murray Photography
Based in: Leeds
{T} 01132 765981
INFO@SIMONMURRAY.COM
WWW.SIMONMURRAY.COM

Simon Redhead Photography
Based in: West Sussex
{T} 01903 523003
SIMON.REDHEAD2@NTLWORLD.COM
WWW.REFLECTIVEIMAGES.INFO

Simon Whitehead Photography
Based in: Bristol
{T} 01179 047216
SIMON@GALLERY2C.COM
WWW.GALLERY2C.COM

SJS Photography
Based in: London
{T} 07733 107146
STUART@SJSPHOTO.COM
WWW.SJSPHOTO.COM

Small Screen Showreels
Based in: London
{T} 02088 168896
HEADSHOTS@SMALLSCREENSHOWREELS.CO.UK
WWW.SMALLSCREENSHOWREELS.CO.UK

Soho Headshots
Based in: London
{T} 07958 486051
INFO@SOHOHEADSHOTS.COM
WWW.SOHOHEADSHOTS.COM

Stan Gamester Photography
Based in: Berkshire
{T} 01189 419427
INFO@STANGAMESTER.COM
WWW.STANGAMESTER.COM

State Of Mind Photography
Based in: Sussex
{T} 07776 045171
INFO@STATE-OF-MIND.CO.UK
WWW.STATE-OF-MIND.CO.UK

Steffan Hill Photographer
Based in: Belfast
{T} 02890 245038
INFO@STEFFANHILL.COM
WWW.STEFFANHILL.COM

STEPHANIE DE LENG
BASED IN: LIVERPOOL
{T} 01514 761563
DELENG@BLUEYONDER.CO.UK
WWW.STEPHANIEDELENG.CO.UK

STEPHANIE GIBBONS PHOTOGRAPHY
BASED IN: LONDON
{T} 07985 192059
S.GIBBONS@LIVE.CO.UK
WWW.SMGPHOTOS.CO.UK

STEPHEN PENNELLS PHOTOGRAPHY
BASED IN: LONDON
{T} 07799 268175
STEVE@DOKOFILMS.COM
WWW.STEPHENPENNELLSPHOTO.COM

STEVE LAWTON PHOTOGRAPHY
BASED IN: LONDON
{T} 07973 307487
STEVELAWTON2@MSN.COM
WWW.STEVELAWTON.COM

STEVE MORGAN
BASED IN: YORKSHIRE
{T} 07798 553272
STEVE@STEVEMORGANPHOTO.CO.UK
WWW.STEVEMORGANPHOTO.CO.UK

STEVE ULLATHORNE PHOTOGRAPHY
BASED IN: LONDON
{T} 07961 381969
STEVE@STEVEULLATHORNE.COM
WWW.STEVEULLATHORNE.COM

STRAIGHTFORWARD STILLS
BASED IN: LONDON
{T} 07830 236715
STRAIGHTFORWARD@ME.COM
WWW.STRAIGHTFORWARDHEADSHOTS.CO.UK

STUART ALLEN PHOTOGRAPHY
BASED IN: LONDON
{T} 07776 258829
INFO@STUARTALLENPHOTOS.COM
WWW.STUARTALLENPHOTOS.COM

STUART CLARKE IMAGES
BASED IN: HERTFORDSHIRE
{T} 07771 864874
STUARTCLARKE@HOTMAIL.COM
WWW.STUARTCLARKEIMAGES.COM

STUART MCALLISTER
BASED IN: SCOTLAND
STUMCA66@GOOGLEMAIL.COM
WWW.SMCALLISTER.CO.UK

STUART NICHOLAS WHITE
BASED IN: LONDON
{T} 02076 350110
STUDIO@STUARTNICHOLASWHITE.COM
WWW.STUARTNICHOLASWHITE.COM

STUDIO MUNRO
BASED IN: LONDON
{T} 07500 223288
MUNRO@STUDIOMUNRO.CO.UK
WWW.STUDIOMUNRO.CO.UK

STUDIO SHOTS
BASED IN: WEST YORKSHIRE
{T} 07796 681935
INFO@STUDIO-SHOTS.CO.UK
WWW.STUDIO-SHOTS.CO.UK

STUDIO TIME PHOTOGRAPHERS
BASED IN: LONDON
{T} 02072 412816
INFO@STUDIOTIMEPHOTO.COM
WWW.STUDIOTIMEPHOTO.COM

STUDIO TWELVE PHOTOGRAPHY
BASED IN: LANCASHIRE
{T} 01257 271651
ILOVEMRPLUG@HUSHMAIL.COM
WWW.STUDIOTWELVE.CO.UK

STUDIOIV
BASED IN: WEST SUSSEX
{T} 01903 251060
GLEN@STUDIOIV.CO.UK
WWW.STUDIOIV.CO.UK

STUDIOU
BASED IN: LONDON
{T} 02082 017567
INFO@STUDIOU.CO.UK
WWW.STUDIOU.CO.UK

SUKEY PARNELL
BASED IN: LONDON
{T} 02073 285760
SUKEY@SUKEYPARNELL.COM
WWW.SUKEYPARNELL.COM

SUZANNAH LEA PHOTOGRAPHY
BASED IN: SURREY
{T} 07702 839995
INFO@SUZANNAH-LEA-PHOTOGRAPHY.COM
WWW.SUZANNAH-LEA-PHOTOGRAPHY.COM

TIGER SHOOTS BACK
BASED IN: HERTS
{T} 07968 420466
PETER@TIGERSHOOTSBACK.CO.UK
WWW.TIGERSHOOTSBACK.CO.UK

TIM BOWDEN PHOTOGRAPHY LTD
BASED IN: LONDON
{T} 07831 397096
T.BOWDEN@NETCOMUK.CO.UK
WWW.TIMBOWDEN.CO.UK

TIM MOROZZO PHOTOGRAPHY
BASED IN: GLASGOW
{T} 01417 704876
TIM@MOROZZO.CO.UK
WWW.MOROZZO.CO.UK

TIM PARKER PHOTOGRAPHY
BASED IN: LONDON
{T} 07803 293251
TIMPARKER.PHOTO@BTINTERNET.COM
WWW.TIMPARKER-PHOTO.COM

TIME MEDIA PRODUCTION
BASED IN: LONDON
{T} 07876 666060
SHAH@TIMEMEDIAPRODUCTION.COM
WWW.TIMEMEDIAPRODUCTION.COM

TINY STAR PHOTOGRAPHY
BASED IN: CO DURHAM
{T} 07818 233001
TINYSTARPHOTOGRAPHY@HOTMAIL.CO.UK
WWW.TINYSTARPHOTOGRAPHY.CO.UK

TITUS POWELL
BASED IN: LONDON
{T} 07970 972675
TITUSPOWELL@GMAIL.COM
WWW.TITUSPOWELL.COM

TM PHOTOGRAPHY & DESIGN LTD
BASED IN: LONDON
{T} 02085 304382
INFO@TMPHOTOGRAPHY.CO.UK
WWW.TMPHOTOGRAPHY.CO.UK

TOBY AMIES PHOTOGRAPHY
BASED IN: SUSSEX
{T} 07739 108563
STUDIO@PICTUREMAKER.PLUS.COM
WWW.TOBYAMIES.COM

TOBY MERRITT PHOTOGRAPHY
BASED IN: LONDON
{T} 07956 439595
TOBY@TOBYMERRITT.CO.UK
WWW.TOBYMERRITT.CO.UK

TOM HART PHOTOGRAPHY
BASED IN: BIRMINGHAM
{T} 07727 628154
TOM.HART.PHOTOGRAPHY@LIVE.CO.UK
WWW.TOMHARTPHOTOGRAPHY.CO.UK

TONY PREECE PHOTOGRAPHY AT STUDIO 49
BASED IN: LONDON
{T} 07939 139097
TONY.PREECE@GMAIL.COM
WWW.TONYPREECE.COM

TRACEY GIBBS PHOTOGRAPHY LTD
BASED IN: MANCHESTER
{T} 01617 878404
INFO@TRACEYGIBBS.CO.UK
WWW.TRACEYGIBBSPHOTOGRAPHY.CO.UK

URBAN ICON
BASED IN: LIVERPOOL
{T} 07989 660459
URBANICON@MAC.COM
WWW.URBANICON.CO.UK

URBANI PHOTOGRAPHY
BASED IN: WEST YORKSHIRE
{T} 07818 711642
LJ@URBANIPHOTOGRAPHY.COM
WWW.URBANIPHOTOGRAPHY.COM

UTOPIA STUDIOS
BASED IN: CHESHIRE
{T} 01614 257512
AMIN@UTOPIASTUDIOS.INFO
WWW.UTOPIASTUDIOS.CO.UK

UTOPIAN PHOTOGRAPHY
BASED IN: GLASGOW
{T} 07976 623880
CHRIS@UTOPIANPHOTOGRAPHY.COM
WWW.UTOPIANPHOTOGRAPHY.COM

V1 INTERNATIONAL
BASED IN: BIRMINGHAM
{T} 07833 300812
VINCENT@V1INTERNATIONAL.COM
WWW.V1INTERNATIONAL.COM

VANESSA VALENTINE PHOTOGRAPHY
BASED IN: HIGHGATE
{T} 07904 059541
VALENTINE.PHOTOGRAPHY@HOTMAIL.COM
WWW.VANESSAVALENTINEPHOTOGRAPHY.COM

VINCENT ABBEY PHOTOGRAPHY
BASED IN: MANCHESTER
{T} 01618 606794
VABBEY@YAHOO.COM
WWW.VINCENTABBEY.CO.UK

VINCENZO PHOTOGRAPHY
BASED IN: LONDON
{T} 02083 720488
INFO@VINCENZOPHOTOGRAPHY.COM
WWW.VINCENZOPHOTOGRAPHY.COM

VLADAS BIJEIKA PHOTOGRAPHY
BASED IN: SUTTON
{T} 07775 582596
VLADASBJ@GOOGLEMAIL.COM
WWW.VLADASBIJEIKA.CO.UK

VOODOO PHOTOS
BASED IN: BELFAST
{T} 02890 237577
CIARAN@CIARANONEILLPHOTOGRAPHY.COM
WWW.VOODOOPHOTOS.COM

VPHOTOGRAPHIC LTD
BASED IN: HERTS
{T} 07883 297818
PAUL.MARSHALL@VPHOTOGRAPHIC.CO.UK
WWW.VPHOTOGRAPHIC.CO.UK

WAVENEY PHOTOGRAPHY
BASED IN: SUFFOLK
{T} 07837 184844
GAVIN.MORRIS@GMAIL.COM
WWW.WAVENEYPHOTOGRAPHY.COM

WEBHEADSMEDIA.NET
BASED IN: DEVON
{T} 07722 361672
KARL.WEBER@VIRGIN.NET
WWW.WEBHEADSMEDIA.NET

WILL DENNEHY PHOTOGRAPHY
BASED IN: LONDON
{T} 02084 281722
WILL@WILLPHOTO.CO.UK
WWW.WILLPHOTO.CO.UK

WILLIAM DAVID
BASED IN: LEICESTER
{T} 07962 449582
WILD@WILLIAMDAVID.CO.UK
WWW.WILDMODELS.CO.UK

WOLF MARLOH
BASED IN: LONDON
{T} 07976 329506
HEADSHOTS@10X8.COM
WWW.10X8.COM

YIANNIS PHOTOGRAPHY
BASED IN: LONDON
{T} 07826 780838
YIANNIS.PORTRAITS@GMAIL.COM
WWW.YIANNISPHOTOGRAPHY.CO.UK

YURI PIRONDI
BASED IN: LONDON
{T} 07768 794381
YURIPIRONDI@GOOGLEMAIL.COM
WWW.YURIPIRONDI.CO.UK

ZACHARY HUNT PHOTOGRAPHY
{T} 01773 826872
CCP@ZACHARYHUNT.CO.UK
WWW.ZACHARYHUNT.CO.UK

Showreels

With broadband connection speeds improving and DVDs cheap to reproduce, showreels have become an increasingly important way to market yourself. A showreel provides "moving image evidence" of what you are like as a performer. Without it, a casting director or agent can only assess you on the strength of your CV and photograph, which by their two-dimensional nature can only provide part of the picture.

When it comes to all types of screen casting, nothing is more helpful to those casting than being able to see you on camera. So much so, that increasingly casting professionals will only call a person in to audition if they have seen their showreel beforehand. The showreel makes up a key third of your marketing or "job application" package.

Content

Showreels are usually created from a collection of past work, showcasing your range as an actor. Ideally your showreel will consist of clips from broadcast work. However, if you don't have sufficient clips from your body of work you could consider getting a showreel made for you from pieces shot specifically for the showreel. Many of the leading showreel companies now offer 'shoot from scratch' services in which they'll work with you to shoot your choice of scenes. If you have some previous material but not all of it is usable, showreel producers can also help you combine this with material shot from scratch. Some also offer script consultation and direction which are worth considering to ensure you choose suitable material and to get the perfect performance.

When thinking about scripts and scenes it's generally better to concentrate on scenes showing you playing characters you are likely to be cast as. So rather than trying to show your entire range in a showreel, focus on portraying these characters – play to and showcase your existing strengths. Too much versatility makes it difficult for a casting director to picture you in the role, so put your best character forward.

Always use the services of a professional company; there is an art to putting together a professional looking showreel. A showreel that looks like it was cobbled together by a friend won't do you any favours. It really is worth going to the expense of using a professional company which specialises in showreels for actors.

Before deciding on a company, try to view samples of their work to give you an idea of the quality of the finished product. As ever, if you can get personal recommendations from other actors you know, so much the better.

Make the showreel informative and entertaining as this will help maintain a casting director's attention. The first 30 seconds of your showreel are the most important. It's often sensible to start with a brief collage of the work about to be shown, ensuring the casting director gets a quick overview of your talent right from the start.

Alternatively, you might consider opening with a still of your headshot or a long close up, over which you can place your name. At all points in your showreel it should be clear that the focus is on you as it is you who is being showcased, not the other actors. With this in mind, include plenty of close-ups.

Length
Your showreel should ideally be three to four minutes long, with the maximum length of each clip not exceeding 60 seconds, ideally only 30 seconds and of varied length (see box on p101). Try not to exceed six minutes in length; casting directors don't have the time to watch a mountain of showreels from start to finish. Better a pacey three-minute reel than a five-minute one which seems to drag. Keep it clean, keep it simple and keep it relevant.

Format
If you are considering creating a new showreel, you'll want to end up with both a DVD (or CD-ROM) version of your showreel which you can post to casting directors and a 'streamed' version which you can upload to your website or to websites which offer a hosting service.

The DVD version of your showreel will look pretty standard – but take the time to ensure the box and DVD come with personalised designs which have your name and contact number clearly visible. As most showreel companies will charge you for subsequent copies of your DVD, take the price of DVD duplication services into account when selecting a service provider.

Streamed or internet showreels should be in wmv (Windows Media Video) or QuickTime format, and a typical file size for a two- to three-minute showreel should be around 6Mb.

Usually a showreel editing facility will be able to handle all the regular formats but check with them beforehand if you have a more untypical format eg VHS-NTSC (used in the United States).

Your contact details should be clearly visible at the start and end of the showreel and on all packaging. Where possible try to include your headshot on the CD cover or DVD case.

Costs

Editing previous material is likely to be charged by the hour (probably between £40 and £80 ph), which is why getting your material organised properly important is vital.

If you need material shot from scratch, it will probably cost a few hundred pounds for each scene – make sure you know where you stand on this before proceeding with a showreel company, and discuss all the details with them. Ideally you won't want to film too many new scenes, in the hope that you'll soon have new material from real work that can be spliced into a updated showreel in due course.

Given that the costs for producing a showreel are high, it's vital that you choose a company with suitable experience of working with actors, and that the end results present you in the best possible way.

Showreels – your ace card

Content kindly supplied by The Actor's One Stop Shop
www.actorsone-stopshop.com

A showreel is probably the most powerful marketing tool you can have. Think about it, a friend may go on about how wonderful an actor is in this or that movie for months but it's only when you see them move and speak that you can judge for yourself the strength of their performances.

From a casting perspective setting up auditions is hard work and you can only really see about twenty five actors in a day, with showreels you can see a hundred plus, and the fact that you're seeing performances rather than just social chin wagging leads to a more meritorious system where people can be cast primarily for their talent.

Then there's the agent angle. If you're without an agent then you'll want one and if you're with an agent then you'll want a better one. Either way they'll need to see what they're buying into and how can they represent you if they don't know what you can do?

So now you're sold. You want a showreel but it all seems very complicated. No it isn't. Let's start at the base line: Do you have material from past films? If yes then obviously you'd like that work to feature on your showreel or if not the way to go is to shoot something from scratch. Let's take each case one at a time.

1. Edited from existing material showreels
All that's going to happen is that you're going to sit down and review your work. Making notes of your best scenes and using your player's counter to note where they start and end. You'll only want at most 3 clips from any particular production and in total you really don't need more than 14 clips from all of your productions.

Then you're going into an editing suite and these clips are going to be loaded onto a computer and carved down to a pacy and interesting showreel lasting between 3 and 4 minutes. What could be easier?

As regards cost it'll be by the hour, some facilities offer 'all in' prices but then say 'up to x number of hours and then it'll be by the hour' so it's the same thing really. If you can't go above a certain price then tell the editor beforehand, if they're experienced they should be able to keep to it – be aware though that if you'd like them to do that they'll probably need to have quite a free reign on the showreel.

The next most common thing I hear said is that the actor's material is very weak and they're waiting for stuff. Again don't worry, until you see just how powerful editing is in the hands of a good editor you won't really appreciate what can be achieved. Low budget and student films are often very badly put together, re-cutting, editing to reduce other characters, adding music can all give even the most uninspiring scene unbelievable muscle. It's a bit like what can be achieved on photos with air brushing and treating – spots, wrinkles all gone! Beautiful tan and alluring eyes guaranteed! Editing is just as powerful.

As regards as how many good scenes you need the answer is very simple, just one. If we hear you interacting with another character in just one scene then other scenes may not even need words, their presence is just to strengthen your body of experience or perhaps the quality of productions you've been in.

About that promised copy where you had a strong role that you've been waiting for for months? My advice is don't. Get something together now. If you go to a professional outfit they should keep your showreel so that new credits can be easily added like you do to your CV – it makes an incredible difference once casters and agents can see your moving image so you don't want to delay even a few months only discover the clip you've been waiting for is less than hoped.

But supposing you simply haven't been on camera or it really is genuinely a bit below par? That's where the might of 'Shot-from-scratch' comes in.

2. Shot from scratch showreels

Again it's all very simple. Scenes are shot and edited exactly as if they actually did come out of films and then put together on a showreel, so it looks as if they came from produced films and the end result appears like an edited from existing material showreel.

If you go to a company that can supply you with suitable scripts to choose from, actors, a director and they're prepared to produce the showreel then it should be all very easy, enjoyable even and moreover give you a real chance to expand your acting talent into the bargain. One of the key things is to avoid the temptation of directing yourself, characters are always more three dimensional and interesting under the guidance of a professional, experienced drama director, plus they'll give you an idea of what works and what doesn't as well as what's feasible to shoot on your budget.

The scenes can be integrated with existing work, just used along with other shot scenes or indeed just used as a single scene by itself. One actor reported back a few months ago that he'd just been cast in a central role in a feature film based on a single simple scene.

Anyhow that should be enough to give you an overview of showreels and what they're about. I could go on for hours; UK format, USA format, splash montages, attention spans, musical flows, lyrical interaction between credits, establishment of primary character, use of action material, gluing section techniques, use of model style shots, target markets and so on, and on, and on... Which you might expect from someone who can in all likelihood claim to have made more showreels than anyone on the planet! There's a lot to it, but concentrate on the points and advice listed above and you'll be well on your way to putting together the most powerful tool in your professional acting arsenal – your showreel. Good luck!

Voicereels

Chapter kindly provided by Cut Glass Productions (www.cutglassproductions.com).

If you want to get into the voiceover industry, your first step will be to create a top quality voicereel to send out to agents, production companies and casting directors. This is your chance to showcase your vocal abilities, and is a powerful 'calling card'. A well put together reel makes an impression - and you won't be considered for voiceover jobs without one.

It's important to get your voicereel right. Even if you have a fantastic voice, if the reel is badly produced or directed, drags on for 10 minutes with boring material, uses the same backing music/scripts as hundreds of other showreels, or doesn't show any variation, it is likely to end up in a frustrated agent's bin!

Your voicereel should showcase your natural voice as much as possible, so it's a good idea to make the most of your natural accent and voice qualities. If a casting director wants a 'northern voice' they usually prefer it to be a genuine one. Occasionally, however, a job may call for one actor to voice several different voices – and if you do have an excellent ear for accents it might be a good idea to try these out in a single animation style piece/narration on your voicereel.

The recording session
You should feel comfortable and relaxed in your chosen recording environment. It is vital that you are given enough time to experiment with material, especially if you are recording a voicereel for the first time.

Good direction and production skills are vital. The director should gently guide you in what suits your voice, what is working for your voice, and what isn't. You might find your voice is just right for intimate, soft-sell ads and promos, but not punchy hard-sell. You may also discover your voice and delivery style is extremely well suited to documentary work. It should be a one-to-one journey – a flexible, creative process between you and the person directing the session.

Recording a voicereel isn't something that should be rushed through in a single hour, or even two. If you are in a studio that rushes you in and out of the door, you probably aren't getting enough guidance, help and direction, and it will be obvious on the finished product.

Your voicereel

Your finished voicereel should be around four minutes long. Any longer, and you will have lost the casting director's attention. It should be edited, together with music and sound effects, to show your voice to its maximum potential. Your reel should contain a mix of commercial ads, documentaries and narrations. A punchy 60-90 second 'montage' that sits at the beginning of the reel is also a good idea, to give a quick snapshot of your abilities.

If you are looking to get into radio drama at the BBC, they ask for a different kind of voicereel altogether, featuring dramatic pieces and no commercials. This should still be punchy, show your best possible vocal range, and be well produced.

Commercial opportunities

In an age of high-speed broadband, having a voicereel to hand has become an important way for an actor to market themselves. The industry has expanded so much that you don't need to be a high profile celebrity in order to get voiceover work. Digital technology has opened up endless possibilities for the voiceover artist: mobile entertainment, animations, narration, e-learning… and there are more commercials, documentaries and factual entertainment shows than ever before.

Although lucrative, the voiceover industry is a competitive industry, just like acting. If you are prepared to market yourself, have a great voice and an individual, well-produced showreel, you are several steps ahead of the competition!

Auditions & interviews

When attending interviews or auditions it's vital to be punctual: plan how you are going to get there, and allow extra contingency time for unexpected delays en route. The casting director may well have allocated specific time slots and the last thing you want is to miss yours. If you're a little early, you will have time to compose yourself.

Arrive well-presented and ready to perform, and introduce yourself clearly. Make eye contact with the casting director and try not to be too nervous. There are ways of dressing appropriately for a part, in such a way as to chime with what you think the character might wear, but unless it's been specifically requested, which is unusual, you should turn up as yourself rather than in costume. First impressions count and are difficult to overturn.

Preparation can really help in building confidence. Learn your lines, practice the piece again and again until you know the words backwards and inhabit the character instinctively. It's difficult to overemphasise how much familiarity with your material can help build confidence and ultimately deliver a good performance.

Under-preparing can have disastrous consequences. Not only will it make you look unprofessional, but if you go into the audition knowing you've not prepared then you may very well find your mouth drying and the words disappearing while the casting director is looking on and, if not shaking their head, then wondering why you're wasting their time.

Practise in front of your friends – in a lot of cases, you may think you have learned a monologue, but as soon as you are in that audition, you have so many distractions that it's easy to forget your lines. Practice might not make perfect but it will sure go a long way! Practice pacing yourself to avoid being breathless or too ponderous.

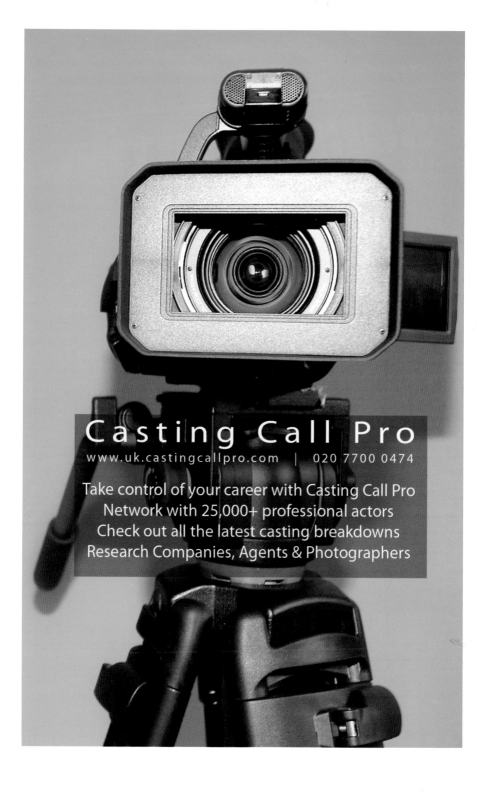

CLEVER BOY MEDIA.

"SCREEN ACTING CLOSE UP"

A DEFINITIVE DVD GUIDE FOR ACTORS

NIC PHILLIPS has been a successful TV director and producer for more than thirty years, and his recent credits include **'Eastenders'** and **'My Family'**. Producer **TIM KENT** was an agent for more than 10 years and now runs a busy production company at **Pinewood Film Studios**. **CATHERINE WILLIS** is a prominent UK casting director with a host of prestigious credits including **'Taggart'** and **'Criminal Justice'**.

Nic, Tim and Catherine have joined forces to produce **"Screen Acting Close Up"**, a DVD designed as a resource for actors of all levels of experience.

THE DVD HAS THREE SEPARATE SECTIONS:

1. AUDITION WITH CONFIDENCE: Catherine provides practical advice on how an actor should prepare for a screen audition. She shows the casting process most commonly in use today, outlines ways to avoid the pitfalls of interview 'overkill', and offers valuable advice to actors on their approach to casting.

2. SCREEN ACTING CLOSE UP: Nic explains some basic technical skills an actor needs to master to perform successfully for the camera. In specially created scenes a group of young actors illustrate some of the fundamental 'do's and don'ts' of screen craft.

3. MAKING THE BUSINESS YOUR BUSINESS: Tim offers extensive, practical advice on finding an agent, running an acting career, and answers many of actors' most-frequently-asked questions.

RRP £29.99 **BUY DIRECT FROM www.screenactingcloseup.com or call 01753 650 651**

British Institute of Professional Photography

FRAZER ASHFORD

ASSOCIATE OF THE INSTITUTE OF PROFESSIONAL PHOTOGRAPHY

ASSOCIATE OF THE ROYAL PHOTOGRAPHIC SOCIETY

CASTING / HEADSHOT
PHOTOGRAPHY

www.castingphotography.co.uk
frazer@frazerashford.com

0844 351 0046
0777 6174400

FAST TRACK YOUR ACTING CAREER!

Before you select your casting / headshot photographer you should read the **_free_** e-book:

"TEN THINGS EVERY ACTOR SHOULD KNOW BEFORE COMMISSIONING CASTING HEADSHOTS!"

This **_free_** e-book you will show you:

1 - How to find the right photographer...

2 - How to get the most from your headshot session...

3 - How to avoid getting your pictures tossed straight into the bin...

Visit **www.castingphotography.co.uk** and complete the request form. The **_free_** e-book will then be on its way without obligation to your inbox. You will then be more aware of what it takes to help get your career into the fast lane!

Koval Studio

www.piotrkowalik.co.uk

info@piotrkowalik.co.uk 07946323631

ALRA and ALRA North

ALRA, the Academy of Live and Recorded Arts, is pleased and excited to announce the launch of ALRA North, a northern base for ALRA. We are delighted to be the first CDS Drama School to offer regional training together with training at our London home.

ALRA North will be situated in Wigan, with an intake of students from September 2010. The many producing theatres, TV centres and radio studios of the North West are all within easy reach. London is less than two hours away by train.

Course delivery will be identical to ALRA's London base, but with a substantially lower fee structure, due to the lower running costs in the North-West of the country.

For more information, please contact us on info@alra.co.uk, or 020 8870 6475.

ALRA North is currently accepting expressions of interest from tutors and directors.

www.alra.co.uk

Your £125 Spotlight package

Sessions are in and around my London studio, lasting around one and a half hours and I take from 150 - 200 images.

Lots of time for 2 or 3 changes of hairstyle and clothes.

All session images on two discs. One sent to you and one to your agent for viewing and selection.

Your choice of three images printed by myself to "10 x 8".

These same images burned to a third disc for you.

I will email jpegs on request.

See you soon...!

> *My session with Philip was an enjoyable experience. He allowed me as much time and as many clothing changes etc as I wanted and made me feel totally comfortable throughout. He has the ability to guide you gently towards a variety of good shots without being too instructive. He takes plenty of photos but each one seems to be thought out rather than just snapping away hoping for a result. Needless to say, I would highly recommend him and suggest that his prices represent very good value for money. I got prints of my chosen shots and all the shots on disc within 48 hours too...* Russ Bain

Philip Wade Photography
88 Engelfield Road, Islington, London, N1 3LG
T: 020 7226 3088 M: 07956 599691 pix@philipwade.com
www.philipwade.com

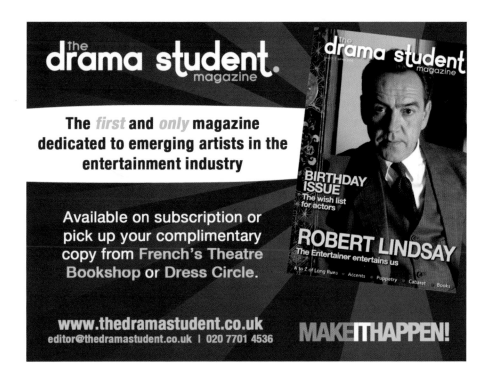

Auditions

In the audition you'll often be expected to have prepared two contrasting pieces, of about two to three minutes each, to show your range. You may have been given some guidance beforehand indicating the style of piece to perform, or you may have a shortlist of speeches/scenes from which you can pick. If you have free range to choose, select something with which you're familiar, a scene or speech you can contextualise and a character you know and care about. In addition to these prepared pieces you may also be asked to sight-read a scene or monologue.

If you're unsure whether or not to address your monologue to the panel or to a spot on the wall, the best thing to do is to ask. Some people hate it when you address a monologue to them, others don't mind. The key is to determine which they would prefer before you start. If they ask you not to address the monologue to them, then pick a spot on the wall a little above their heads.

Take a couple of seconds to gather yourself before you start and when you finish your monologue, don't say "that's it!", don't apologize and don't make excuses, just take a second or two to pause and the panel ought to know when you have finished.

You're bound to be nervous but try and remain relaxed and confident. The people you'll be performing to are not your enemies, they're human beings and they'll appreciate that auditions are a nerve-wracking experience. Make your nerves and energy work for you, harnessing and utilising them to focus on your performance. You may have your own techniques for steadying the nerves such as mental imagery or breathing patterns.

While directors may have pre-conceived notions of what they're looking for, or the part may demand certain physical characteristics, there are numerous cases of actors going into an audition and success-fully making a part their own with their own unique performance.

Be prepared to 'think around the scene' – understanding the motivations of the character will help you perform it, and will also help if you are invited to discuss the scene afterwards.

Auditions for musical theatre can be a somewhat different experience, from a hectic and anonymous 'open audition' for a big West End production down to a more personal presentation. For the former, don't be angry if your singing is cut short – it doesn't necessarily mean they don't like it.

If you are going for a smaller regional show, make sure you talk to director and choreographer equally. Prepare yourself beforehand with a suitable repertoire of different songs, and try to warm your voice up before the actual audition if you can. As for the dance element, the main point will be to see how you move and hold yourself. Don't wear heavy clothing!

Interviews

Do your background research in preparation for an interview. Find out about the director and as much as you can about the production. Consider other productions the director has undertaken and actors they have worked with. Have they a particular style? What do you think the character is like? Prepare yourself for any common questions such as 'Why do you think you're right for the role?'

Talk about the play or the script if you have read it. Show your enthusiasm and keenness and don't be shy about asking any questions you may have. The interview is a two-way process, providing an opportunity for you to find out more as well as for the director/tutor to assess you.

If there is more than one interviewer, address them all equally. Try not to let personalities get in the way – you're here to show your enthusiasm and skills, so there's not point in getting involved in any disagreements (not that you necessarily have to agree with everything they say – informed discussion can be very positive).

Never feel you have to fill every silence: a common mistake in interviews is to talk nervously at nineteen-to-the-dozen.

Rejection

Being considered for a part, auditioning and then not getting the part is a fact of life for an actor. Rejection is inevitable. This can be painful, especially if you were particularly set on a part for which you thought you were perfect. It's something you'll have to get used to. You certainly won't be alone.

It helps to think of it not as rejection, which can cement a negative perception, but rather to think of it along the lines of "I wasn't chosen this time, roll on next time". The reason you weren't chosen may not be to do with your audition; it could be that you weren't, in the end, physically what the director had in mind or that somebody else was absolutely ideal and shone out. Never let being turned down for a part dent your determination to get the next one!

Attending auditions – including those for which you don't get the part – helps to get your name and face out there and may lead to future recalls and auditions.

A-Z of further training

THE ACADEMY OF CREATIVE TRAINING

WWW.ACTBRIGHTON.ORG

{T} 012 7381 8266

INFO@ACTBRIGHTON.ORG

The only Drama School on the South Coast offering a professional actor training, ACT attracts students of all ages and walks of life and enables people to realistically achieve their ambition of a career in the performing arts. Classes are in the evenings and at weekends so that students can continue to meet their working and/or domestic commitments whilst re-training. ACT also offers short courses and a summer school. The ACT team is comprised of highly experienced, passionate and dedicated actors and directors. They bring their own current professional practice into the classroom, relish the opportunity to nurture new talent and are committed to creating a safe, supportive and inspiring creative environment. We run on a non profit making basis so we can offer quality training at affordable rates. Our ethos is to provide access to professional Drama Training for talented individuals who have been unable to follow traditional routes into the acting profession through lack of academic qualifications, financial restrictions or family responsibilities. Students must be 18+ to apply to the Diploma and 16+ for the Foundation and all other adult courses. There is no upper age limit.

THE ACTOR'S CENTRE

WWW.ACTORSCENTRE.CO.UK

{T} 020 7420 3940

ADMIN@ACTORSCENTRE.CO.UK

The Actors Centre was created, by actors for actors, to nurture the art of performance in any media. Our mission is to provide actors with continuing professional development of the highest quality and the opportunity to enhance every aspect of their craft. We seek to enable the pursuit of excellence by promoting high artistic standards across the profession and initiating innovative work, as well as being a friendly meeting place in which actors can share information and exchange ideas. Located in the heart of the West End, we have a membership at any one time of between 2300 and 2500 professional actors. Our premises include five rehearsal studios, a media studio and the Tristan Bates Theatre, a laboratory for innovative new work that place the actor at the heart of the creative process. We also have a licensed café bar, The Green Room, which provides a warm welcome for members and their guests throughout the day and into the evening. All our workshops and classes are led by distinguished practitioners and expert teachers, including many actors and directors who are at the forefront of the film, television and theatre industries. We aim to equip actors for every kind of work from classical theatre to prime time TV by preserving vital elements of the craft that are under threat, as well as to keeping them in touch with current practices and with what's coming next. Since we believe that artistic development should coexist and overlap with the making of new work and the freedom to experiment, many of the workshops that we offer are explorations of work-in-progress, new writing and radical innovations in form and content. We actively promote relationships with the writers and directors who we believe will shape the future of TV, theatre and film, providing them with the space and time to try out new ideas. The Actors Centre runs approximately 1700 classes and workshops a year, and, thanks to the generosity of our funders, they are great value for money.

There is generally a maximum of twelve members enrolled on each workshop as well as a wide range of classes offering one-to-one tuition. Four types of membership options are available.

Actors Centre North

WWW.NORTHERNACTORSCENTRE.CO.UK
{T} 0161 819 2513
INFO@NORTHERNACTORSCENTRE.CO.UK
The ACN caters for those living or working in the North West of England, Yorkshire, North Wales and the North Midlands. Classes run in Manchester,

Liverpool, Leeds and Harrogate. The ACN gained its independence in 1995 having previously been funded through the London Actors Centre. The ACN provides workshops for actors and other professionals in theatre, television, film and radio to enable them to continuously maintain and develop their craft once their initial training has been completed. Areas covered include physical, vocal, studio techniques, characterisation, approaches to specific styles, genres and authors, career management. Postgraduate workshops in such skills are not run by any other educational institution in the area. Current Actors Centre members on tour or working in the North of England can take advantage of classes run by the Actors Centre North for just a £5 admin fee for 3-month membership (normal 6-month membership is £14).

The Actor's Temple

WWW.ACTORSTEMPLE.COM
{T} 020 3004 4537
INFO@ACTORSTEMPLE.COM
The Actors' Temple is the largest community of independent actors in the UK with a shared ethos and technique. Our aim is to become the leading influence in dramatic film making in this country and to revive the tradition of the repertory theatre whereby company members continuously rehearse and produce plays. We specialise in techniques created by Sanford Meisner.

The training fully develops your emotional depth and spontaneity, and the range of your imagination. It provides you with a toolkit which is applicable across the full variety of roles and genres which you will encounter in your career. Acting is a never ending search, a true art form and arguably the most complex and challenging of all the art forms. The full training is only the beginning of this journey and it's the constant exploration over years and years of practice that defines the true actor.

THE CITY LIT

WWW.CITYLIT.AC.UK
{T} 020 7492 2600
{F} 020 7492 2735
INFOLINE@CITYLIT.AC.UK

The City Lit offers a wide range of classes including preparing for auditions, the Alexander technique, the Meisner technique, method acting, Stanislavski workshop, accents, sightreading, speaking Shakespeare, Acting in Chekhov, Acting in Shakespeare, acting for radio, clowning and performance, stage-fighting and more.

OLD VIC NEW VOICES CLUB

WWW.OLDVICTHEATRE.COM/OVNV/ASSOCIATES
{T} 020 7928 2651
NEWVOICES@OLDVICTHEATRE.COM

For those embarking on a professional career in theatre, the Old Vic New Voices Club offers actors, directors, producers and writers, aged 18-25, the opportunity to learn from industry professionals, receive support for projects they are passionate about, and to network with like-minded peers. Become an Associate Member of Old Vic New Voices and you will receive direct updates from us on all forthcoming Projects. We have a year round calendar of exciting events, workshops and other opportunities for you to help build your career, network with like-minded young artists and showcase your talents.

Eligibility is for any member of IdeasTap between the ages of 18-25 living in London.

THEATRE ROYAL HAYMARKET, MASTERCLASSES

www.masterclass.org.uk
{T} 020 7389 9660
info@masterclass.co.uk

Set up by the Theatre Royal Haymarket in 1998 to give young people the chance to learn from and be inspired by leading artists from theatre, film and TV, the hugely successful Masterclass programme has now welcomed over 50,000 people aged 17-30.

With a year-round programme of free talks, workshops, special projects and career advice sessions, Masterclass is a unique charity providing exceptional creative opportunities for young people interested in all aspects of theatre from acting and directing to writing and producing. The impressive list of over

180 past masters includes: Helen Mirren, Nicholas Hytner, Kwame Kwei-Armah, Deborah Warner, Patricia Hodge, Alan Ayckbourn and Derek Jacobi. All have shared their knowledge, enthusiasm and expertise with young people as part of Masterclass at the Haymarket.

YOUNGBLOOD

HTTP://YOUNGBLOOD.CO.UK

{T} 020 7193 3207

INFO@YOUNGBLOOD.CO.UK

YoungBlood offers a wide range of stage combat training to actors through intensive courses and ongoing classes. Basic stage combat classes include the most common stage combat techniques, a fundamental understanding of the principals of movement involved in stage combat, safe practices in rehearsal and performance, and teach actors to deepen their performance as fighters and actors. Intensives generally span a week or longer, enabling the actor to achieve a strong base of fight skills. Intensives include the option of certification through the BADC or another internationally recognised stage combat association. Ongoing Classes meet once a week. You prepare for certification with the BADC or another internationally recognised stage combat association. In the words of Tim Klotz, Director, "If you come on a foundation or pre-professional course with YoungBlood then the training is gentle and encouraging. If you are pursuing a professional qualification with YoungBlood you will train hard. You will probably love it."

Online casting services

In the last few years, with the rise of the Internet and the ubiquity of Broadband, online casting services have really come into their own. They can be a great tool for actors wishing to be proactive and take charge of their career. Where traditionally it has been difficult to find information about castings if you didn't have agency representation, online casting services now allow actors to learn about and submit themselves for casting opportunities. The castings going through these services are widespread, covering the entire spectrum of the acting world including film, television, theatre, radio, corporates, commercials, roleplay, Theatre in Education (TIE). While these online services can be a great source of information, it is also worth remembering that many of the top end castings will not be placed through these services.

Many of the online casting services also provide a searchable online directory of members' profiles – effectively an online CV complete with acting credits, physical characteristics and the all important headshot.

Choosing a service

When many services come and go it can be difficult to know how to choose a service. It's well worth doing your research. Check the credentials of the team behind the service. Over the past few years a number of websites have launched, making great claims for themselves, only to disappear, sometimes having made great promises and delivered little. If it's a new company, check that they have their contact details prominently displayed on their website, try Googling them, contact their customer support team. Peer recommendation is one of the strongest indicators of a service's reputation. If you know someone who is using a particular service ask how useful they find it. Does it get many casting breakdowns? Is the site easy to navigate, does the company provide good customer support? Are the subscription rates comparable with other services? Does the service offer other resources? Does the company have a good reputation within the industry, both with actors and casting directors?

Making applications through online casting services

Employers receive hundreds, if not thousands, of applications through casting services every day. It's very important therefore, as in any other industry, that your cover letter sells you in the best possible way - after all, you want to give the employer a reason to glance at your CV over everyone else's.

- DO: Tailor your cover according to the type of work. It's fair to say that commercial castings, for example, will be so biased according to 'look' that the cover letter is virtually irrelevant and need only be very short, although if you've been in commercials before it never hurts to mention it.

- DO: Sell yourself. What training or skills do you have that are relevant? What roles have you played in the past that would make you well-suited for the part on offer? Have you done that type of work in the past? The whole point of the cover letter is to highlight the work on your CV that will help you get the role, so that the employer doesn't have to pick through your whole CV to find it for themselves.

- DO: Read the brief thoroughly. You don't want to miss out on mentioning something specific they ask for - you also don't want to ignore a very important requirement that you don't meet.

- DO: Chek you're speling. You could be Sir Ian McKellen, but you'll look more like Dirk Diggler if you can't put a sentence together. It's a good idea to write your actual letter in a program like Word or TextEdit which can check spelling and grammar as you go along. You can copy and paste it in when you're done, but...

- DO: Be careful if you're 'Copy and Paste'-ing. You won't look too clever if you send a cover letter to the BBC talking about how much you like ITV's drama output.

- DO: Include any information the employer has specifically requested. Whether it's contact details, dress size, showreels, languages or whatever, you MUST make sure it's in there. If it's not, it's likely your application will simply be rejected as soon as it's opened.

- DO: Be realistic.

- DON'T: Ignore the employer's requirements ('I know I don't fit the bill, but I thought I'd apply anyway /in case you have any future projects'). If you're not what they're looking for then you're not going to change their minds. It may sound harsh, but this is a complete waste of your times and theirs. They may remember you, but only as someone who doesn't listen to what they're told, so they probably won't want to work with you in the future.

- DON'T: Say 'my experience speaks for itself'. Right now it's saying 'I'm too lazy/arrogant to outline why I'm suitable'. This doesn't signify you'll be a terrific person to work alongside.

- DON'T: Apply for something when you can't make the dates. If the employer hasn't given you a timeframe then fair enough, but don't assume that they can (or will) adjust their schedule to accommodate you. They're more likely to find it extremely annoying.

- DON'T: Get too chatty. A little personality is fine, but remember you're a professional writing to another professional, so leave the text speak and smilies on Facebook.

- DON'T: Send it until you're happy. Realistically you only have one shot at cover letters, so make sure you're 100% sure that it's the best you can do before hitting 'send'.

List of online casting services

Casting Call Pro

WWW.UK.CASTINGCALLPRO.COM

INFO@CASTINGCALLPRO.COM

{T} 020 7700 0474

Casting Call Pro (CCP) was established in 2004 and offers an online profile, casting alerts, and a variety of useful resources such as online directories of agents (including those with open books), photographers, employers, schools, and theatre companies. In addition, members can contact one another and ask advice in the forum. CCP currently lists 25,000+ actors and is used by hundreds of production companies, casting directors and employers. A profile listing in the directory is free. Premium membership is £17+VAT per month or £130+VAT for a year.

CastNet

WWW.CASTINGNETWORK.CO.UK

ADMIN@CASTINGNETWORK.CO.UK

{T} 020 8420 4209

Founded in 1997, CastNet offers members a profile in a searchable online directory and access to the casting breakdowns available through the site. You must have trained at accredited drama school and have a minimum of three professional acting credits. Subscription is apporximately £6.50 per week. Please check their website for current prices.

CastWeb

WWW.CASTWEB.CO.UK

INFO@CASTWEB.CO.UK

[T] 020 7720 9002

Established in 199, CastWeb is an email-based casting breakdown service. Recognised industry-wide, CastWeb produces regular daily updates for subscribers detailing work available on stage screen and in print. Over 1,600 Casting Professionals send out their casting and audition requirements via CastWeb. Please check their website for current prices.

Production and Casting Report (PCR)

WWW.PCRNEWSLETTER.COM

INFO@PCRSUBSCRIPTIONS.COM

{T} 020 7549 2578

Established for over 40 years, PCR – Production Casting Report – is a guide to auditions, castings and crew calls in the world of film, television and theatre. The monthly subscription is approximately £21-22.

SPOTLIGHT

WWW.SPOTLIGHTCD.COM

INFO@SPOTLIGHT.COM

{T} 020 7437 7631

Founded in 1927, Spotlight lists more than 30,000 actors and is used by thousands of TV, film, theatre and radio professionals. Once registered you'll appear in The Spotlight Book, published annually, and have an online profile which you can login to with a pin number to keep your details up to date. You will also have access to Spotlight's casting breakdown service, The Spotlight Link. You don't need to have an agent to be a member of Spotlight, but "Spotlight only accepts entries from artists who have recognised training and/or professional acting experience". Costs vary depending on when you join. Please contact Spotlight for current rates.

Section 4
Sources of work

Unpaid work

In acting the competition is fierce and paid work doesn't always come thick and fast, so new actors often take on unpaid roles to build their reputation, reviews and experience.

The scale and professionalism of unpaid theatre productions and films varies enormously, from a single person who is writer/director/crew with little or no experience of putting a piece together, to much more professional set-ups with full equipment, sound recordists, lighting camera people, a cast of actors, a director, writer. On unpaid productions you'll often find that it's not just the actors working for free – the crew may also be doing it as a labour of love and to learn more, expand their contacts and CV, just like you.

If you're looking to join in with an unpaid production, it will help to know that other people in the team are aiming for professional careers, too. Don't be tempted into thinking that 'amateur dramatics' will help you keep your hand in, for example: do it for fun by all means, but it is unlikely to help your career progression or boost your CV in a way that the industry will warm to.

Student films
Student films can be a great way of learning; simply by being in front of a camera, working with a script, a director and other actors. Everyone has to start somewhere and some of the people you work with on a student project may go on to be the leading lights of tomorrow.

If you're between jobs they can be a means of keeping your skills sharp and of networking with other actors and industry creatives. (It can be the kind of experience you don't get on a course or in your usual environment working with actors and technicians with whom you're familiar.)

As well as the actual on-set experiences, the film is likely to be viewed by a whole host of other people in the business, actors, teachers, directors, so it's another showcase for your talents.

The nature of the project could be anything from an end-of-year student film to a low/no budget film which may go on to get some kind of distribution or lead to members of the cast and crew gaining representation and the film reaching a wider audience (eg via a short film competition), gaining greater exposure for all involved. Ask the film-makers if they have signed up to the Protecting Actors Agreement (www.protectingactors.org).

Another option is to 'go it alone' with your own fringe theatre show at one of the festivals – see Section 5 for some specific advice on this.

The downside
The flip side of unpaid work is that you may find yourself traipsing halfway across the country, working with less than professional cast and crew and all for the grand reward of a copy of the finished film for your collection. A casting agent or director may look at your CV and see only a string of non-paid credits and not give you a second glance.

As with work as an extra (see the next chapter), you run the risk of being pigeon-holed and boxing yourself into a particular type of work, not making the transition from unpaid to paid, professional work. Having said this, most people recognise that you have to start somewhere and you can always omit work from your CV if you feel it won't be to your advantage to include it.

Part-time work

Part-time and temporary work can be a godsend in the acting profession. As well as helping towards the rent it gives you a greater degree of flexibility to attend those all-important interviews and auditions. The obvious drawback with part-time work is that it's not going to let you live like a king or queen.

Part-time jobs usually pay pro rata, so your income will be substantially less than if you were working full time. It's a cliché that the majority of actors take up part-time work in a bar as a waiter or hostess. Like most clichés, there's some truth in it. The shift nature of this and similar types of promotional work you help in fitting auditions around your work commitments.

As well as registering with temping and promotions agencies, a number of which are detailed below, plus corporate role-play firms, there are a number of other avenues you can pursue. Examples include market research and mystery shopping. These types of jobs often pay cash in hand and you're usually looking at between £30 to £50 per hour.

Extra work

Another classic source of part-time work is of course as an extra, 'walk on' or 'supporting' actor. Make no mistake: although there are people who earn some sort of a living doing loads of 'background' work (though they are often not professional actors), it's tiring work, time-consuming and requires keeping unusual hours. TV and film scenes with extras often start at the crack of dawn and go on for ages as a scene is retaken over and over again. You won't get the chance to hob-nob with the stars!

Having said all that, walk-on work can earn you £100 a day, which could be what gets the bills paid, and can be interesting experience particularly if you want to see what TV and film work is like.

Extra work is sometimes advertised in local newspapers, but you will find more opportunities at web directories such as StarNow (**www.starnow.co.uk**) or **www.starsinmyeyes.tv**. Total Talent (**www.total-talent.com**) is a directory where you can list your profile for free for casting directors to look at. There are also numerous specialist agencies for walk-on work. For more information and a list of such agents, see the National Association of Supporting Artistes' Agents at **www.nasaa.org.uk**.

Roleplay & corporate training

In addition to acting for stage, screen and radio there are other professional outlets such as roleplaying and corporate training videos. Roleplaying is now commonplace in the business environment and seen by many companies as a valuable means of motivating and educating their employees, from sales reps through to CEOs and from multinational corporations to local authority departments.

There are companies dedicated to providing roleplay actors to businesses, working with the business on the brief then collaborating with the actors to develop tailored roleplay scenarios designed to help the company achieve its aims. Typically, workshops will be run by a trainer aided by actors and delivered to an audience who will usually be asked to participate. The workshops may be run with the aim of improving the morale of employees or instructing them on very specific skills which will be employed in their work, such as sales, customer support techniques or preparing for and giving presentations.

This kind of work puts you in front of an audience and requires you to get into character, improvise and interact, skills vital to the actor. And of course it can carry you through the lean times between roles. Equity doesn't cover or advise on rates for roleplay as it doesn't fall within their categorisation of professional acting work, so you'll sometimes find rates of pay are quite low.

Many businesses also find confident and outgoing actors helpful at trade shows, exhibitions and for marketing presentations to help demonstrate new products and services to the trade or the public.

A-Z of roleplay companies

ASHLEY CALAGHAN TRAINING
0208 741 4900
INFO@ACT-ROLEPLAY.COM
WWW.ACT-ROLEPLAY.COM
We have over 15 years experience delivering training and personal development programmes for industry. The use of specially trained actors to play roles is widely recognised as a powerful methodology to help tackle people issues in the work place.

ACTIVATION
0208 783 9494
WWW.ACTIVATION.CO.UK
INFO@ACTIVATION.CO.UK
Drawing on skills of professional actors, writers , trainers and facilitators, we work in many areas of training and development. We enable our clients to communicate a wide range of issues and then work with them to develop the skills needed to make change work.

ACTORS IN INDUSTRY
WWW.ACTORSININDUSTRY.COM
ENQUIRIES@ACTORSININDUSTRY.COM
(0)20 7234 9600
Actors in Industry is the foremost interactive training company in the UK. Our teams of communication experts, trainers, facilitators and roleplayers have been providing memorable and energising training events for clients since 1992. We are creative and innovative and have taken people communication skills and business roleplay to a level that is envied by our competitors.All our teams are hand-picked and trained by Actors in Industry so that individuals are committed and dynamic and with a love and in-depth knowledge of training and development.

AKT PRODUCTIONS LTD
TEL: 020 7495 4043
INFO@AKTPRODUCTIONS.CO.UK
WWW.AKTPRODUCTION.CO.UK
AKT Productions Limited is the UK's premier provider of theatre-based learning resources. With an unequalled track-record of delivery, AKT has been developing high quality learning and development programmes for over 10 years. At AKT we work with our clients to create unique learning and development courses. Each training intervention is designed to the client's own specification. In addition to skilful facilitation and tuition, we use a range of techniques such as roleplay, theatre and video to ensure that participants find learning memorable, engaging and effective.

ACTING-OUT
07852 320 788
INFO@ACTING-OUT.CO.UK
WWW.ACTING-OUT.CO.UK
Acting-Out was formed in 2001 by a group of talented people who had previously developed the work – during the 1990's - as a part of the Derby Playhouse's educational development department.

ACT UP
{T} 020 7924 7701
INFO@ACT-UP.CO.UK
WWW.ACT-UP.CO.UK
Act Up started in 1999. We are an independent organisation specialising in communication and acting training. We run short, part-time courses and bespoke, on-site training for people in business. All the trainers are established, professional actors.

ACTORFACTOR
{T} 01626 336166
INFO@ACTORFACTOR.CO.UK
WWW.ACTORFACTOR.CO.UK
ActorFactor provides many different services; actors, facilitators, theatre skills, drama, performance, forum theatre, role play. ActorFactor uses interactive experiential simulation, such as role play, in an environment that promotes learning and development, ultimately to achieve successful change.

CRAGRATS
:01484 689469
ENQUIRIES@CRAGRATS.COM
WWW.CRAGRATS.COM
CragRats deliver learning and communication programmes, working with people of all ages and disciplines to create engaging learning experiences which appeal to a range of learning styles. Established in 1989, CragRats now has over 300 professionally trained actors involved in their learning experiences.

CREATIVE FORUM
{T} 0845 4301308
INFO@CREATIVEROLEPLAY.CO.UK
WWW.CREATIVEROLEPLAY.CO.UK
Creative Forum offers bespoke training programmes and conference themed performances using theatre, role-play and drama techniques. The training is high impact, memorable and issue led.

DRAMATIC SOLUTIONS
{T} 0845 071 1036
ADMIN@DRAMATICSOLUTIONS.CO.UK
WWW.DRAMATICSOLUTIONS.CO.UK
Dramatic Solutions was created in 2001 when Richard da Costa and Colin Rote met working on a production of Rumplestiltskin. Understanding the power drama has to communicate and the impact it can have on the issues facing business today, they formed the company to utilise this powerful medium in corporate environments. Since then it

has helped numerous businesses achieve their objectives using imaginative and memorable events and programmes focused on improving business performance.

FRANK PARTNERS
WWW.FRANKPARTNERS.CO.UK
01179085384
ANNA@FRANKPARTNERS.CO.UK
NEIL@FRANKPARTNERS.CO.UK
We work in a variety of ways including role – play, forum, theatre, facilitation, games coaching and making films. We bring a wealth of experience , create a safe friendly enviroment, and offer frank challenging feedback which goes right to the heart of the individual and their organization, and we do it with good humour and fun!

IMPACT FACTORY
{T} 020 7226 1877
ENQUIRIES@IMPACTFACTORY.COM
WWW.IMPACTFACTORY.COM
Delivering courses on presentation skills, effective communication, team building, leadership development, public speaking, assertiveness skills, confidence and self esteem to name but a few.

IMPACT UNIVERSAL LTD
{T} 01484 660077
GETINTOUCH@IMPACTUNIVERSAL.COM
WWW.IMPACTUNIVERSAL.COM
Founded on solid principles of quality and reliability, ImpAct on learning has established an enviable reputation for exceeding client expectations. Every training workshop, dramatic presentation or event is thoroughly researched and reviewed to ensure the client brief is accurately interpreted. ImpAct on Learning now services a diverse range of clients in the public sector. It has a committed policy of product development to meet the changing needs of its ever increasing customer base.

INTERACT
{T} 020 7793 7744
INFO@INTERACT.EU.COM
WWW.INTERACT.EU.COM
Interact is the UK's leading exponent of the use of theatre-skills in business. Interact work in close partnership with many organisations in the UK and Europe, to deliver creative solutions to training and development need.

JUST ROLEPLAYERS
07949 936864
HELP@JUSTROLEPLAYERS.COM
WWW.JUSTROLEPLAYERS.COM
Just Roleplayers represents an experienced team of professional actor roleplayers, with a wide cross section of experience, from law to health and from marketing to finance. Professional roleplay is a highly effective and well established method of developing com-munication skills which draws upon the abilities of professional actors to bring reality to roleplay training sessions.

LAUGHLINES
{T} 0845 170 1600
INFO@LAUGHLINES.NET
WWW.LAUGHLINES.NET
Our actors are available for all types of corporate work. We can take on any role-play situation and write the scripts to tailor it for your subject matter. Our work is usually comedy based, as this seems to make a bigger impact. We have many satisfied clients including Shell.

NV MANAGEMENT
0800 083 0281
HELLO@NVMANAGEMENT.CO.UK
WWW.NVMANAGEMENT.CO.UK
Specialists in providing professional actors for the business world and also offering an enticing range of related services including bespoke training films, streaming videos for the web, interactive seminars and much more.

PROACTIVE ROLEPLAY
{T} 020 8761 3804
ENQUIRIES@PROACTIVEROLEPLAY.COM
WWW.PROACTIVEROLEPLAY.COM
ProActive Roleplay looks to bridge the gap between the corporate training industry and the acting profession and is able to do this given the professional backgrounds of the two founder members who trained as professional actors at the Bristol Old Vic Theatre School and since graduating have combined appearing regularly as actors

in theatre and television with their work in the training industry. Prior to embarking on acting careers they both built a considerable history of working in industry, ranging from public sector to private industry management.

THE PERFORMANCE BUSINESS
01932888 885
ACTORS@THEPERFORMANCE.BIZ
WWW.THEPERFORMANCE.BIZ
Our actors are trained to give specific constructive verbal and written feedback. Feedback is linked to specific evidence from the events of the roleplay. This highlights the competencies that require development. We are always looking for actors who can portray authentic business roles. We welcome CV submissions from actors of all types. It is essential that you have worked in a business environment.

ROLEPLAYUK
{T} 01780 761960
INFO@ROLEPLAYUK.COM
ACTING IWWW.ROLEPLAYUK.COM
RoleplayUK's actors are trained to apply specific acting techniques developed by Sanford Meisner. These techniques examine how to react to stimuli provided and encourage a naturalistic reaction rather than a performance.

STEPS

{T} 020 7403 9000

MAIL@STEPSDRAMA.COM

WWW.STEPSDRAMA.COM

Founded in 1992, and originally known as Steps Roleplay, we began by providing professional role players for assessment centres and skills practice. The company has grown and developed since then and we now offer a range of drama based initiatives. The company was re-branded as Steps Drama Learning Development in 2001. We now have a senior management team of six, with support from in-house project managers as well as an administrative and accounting team. All our programmes are designed with the clients' specific learning objectives in mind and delivered by an experienced team of professional actors (all of whom are trained by Steps), facilitators, consultants and associate trainers.

A-Z of pantomime companies

ABERGAVENNY PANTOMIME COMPANY

WWW.ABERGAVENNYPANTOMIME.CO.UK

Abergavenny Pantomime Company is the oldest Pantomime Company in Wales and was established back in 1932, which was known before then as 'The Holy Trinity Company'. Its main aim is to perform a traditional pantomime in order to raise money for local charities. Our pantomimes are generally performed during half-term week in February each year.

THE BEDFORD PANTOMIME COMPANY

WWW.BEDFORDPANTO.INFO

The Bedford Pantomime Company are a community theatre group that exists to produce affordable, family Pantomime in Bedford at Christmas time.

By concentrating on panto and nothing else, we can put together a show that is of really high quality but without losing sight of what panto is all about.

BRUCE JAMES PRODUCTIONS

WWW.BRUCEJAMESPRODUCTIONS.CO.UK

The Company is proud of its friendly atmosphere and tries to make all its productions not only, excellent quality with very high "production values", but also enjoyable for all the casts and crews involved – indeed to make the work that we do as much unlike real work as possible. We believe we are in the privileged position as theatre producers to be doing a job that brings enjoyment and entertainment to theatre-going audiences all over the country and as such we have a duty to bring to the stage productions of the very highest quality.

EXTRAVAGANZA PRODUCTIONS

WWW.PANTO-MIME.CO.UK

Our company is built on the principles of making quality products and providing reliable service. Our diversified product range continues to grow by following trends, improving our standard products, and listening to the customer. Our unique service has established our place in this industry. This allows us to make a distinctive and substantial impact for our clients and audiences.

FAME FACTORY SPOTLIGHT

WWW.FAMEFACTORYSPOTLIGHT.CO.UK

Fame Factory Spotlight's touring pantomimes' are the foremost in this field the opposition is not just behind us, it's not even on the same page! All our scripts have been written by our team of skilled writers, and they are all tried and tested and are proven to be popular, yet they still keeps them fresh and new every year, with popular and original songs up to date jokes and remarks always keeping the scripts topical and relevant, yet never losing sight of the tradition of good clean family pantomime.

JORDAN PRODUCTIONS

WWW.JORDANPRODUCTIONSLTD.CO.UK

We believe in building loyal audiences through consistent delivery of high quality Pantomimes. Maintaining traditions of strong, story-led Pantomimes delivered in a dynamic, exciting way for a 21st Century Audience.

MAGIC LIGHT PRODUCTIONS

WWW.MAGICLIGHTPRODUCTIONS.COM

Our Pantomimes include all of the traditional ingredients . Not like others that only have the singing, dancing and comedy ours also include Magic, UV Puppets, Illusions, Costumed Characters and Special Effects. We use our own scripts written in house and amongst a selection of traditional Pantomime Gags we feature some of our own original clean comedy routines.Blend all of this together with our beautiful costumes , fantastic stage settings, up to date choreography and you will end up with a good quality amazing show full of Fun, Excitement and Adventure that is suitable for all of the family.

PAUL HOLMAN ASSOCIATES

WWW.PAULHOLMANASSOCIATES.CO.UK

PHA is one of the leading theatrical management organisations in the country, with a reputation for presenting high quality, family entertainment. PHA is committed to keeping such entertainment alive and vibrant.   As a theatrical production company, PHA specialises in producing pantomimes, summer seasons and children's shows. PHA also provides educational workshops and coaching facilities, as well as merchandise and costume hire.

PYRAMID PANTOMIMES

WWW.PYRAMIDPANTOMIMES.COM

Every year we strive to write a good old British panto, packed with adventure, excitement, music, dancing and heaps of audience participation! By employing only trained actors, we can ensure performances of the highest standard. Our teams travel to every corner of the country, to almost any sized venue, providing seasonal entertainment for audiences young and old! Pyramid Productions provide a totally self contained show, which can be positioned to fit any size venue. No staging is necessary. All you have to do is provide the children!

169

STOURBRIDGE PANTOMIME COMPANY

WWW.STOURBRIDGEPANTO.CO.UK

SPC was formed in October 1967 and has been presenting a pantomime every January since 1969, at the Town Hall Theatre, Stourbridge - "Aladdin" in January 2008 was our 40th Anniversary production. For the last twenty-five years we have had a professional director/choreographer in the person of Mike Capri and a professional Musical Director, now Barry Hipkiss. Each year we go from strength to strength thanks to the hard work and the dedication of a very strong cast and production team who put the show together in a very short time.

THE PANTO COMPANY

WWW.THEPANTOCOMPANY.COM

The Panto Company launched its first national theatre tours in February 2004 and created a series of issue based plays and workshops for schools on topics such as bullying, and teenage pregnancy. It wasn't long before The Panto Company was providing and managing entertainment teams at holiday centres up and down the country; devising and staging enterprise and training events for organisations such as Business Link, One North East and Job Centre Plus; and being commissioned to write and deliver new shows for SureStart and Health Action Zone.

Theatre in Education

Theatre in Education (TIE) uses theatre to explore educational or social issues with children and young people. Specialist TIE companies often travel around the country, presenting workshops at schools, arts centres, community halls or smaller local theatres, and can provide an ongoing source of work for the suitably motivated actor. TIE programmes have traditionally covered issues such as racism or gender, but nowadays can equally focus on issues such as road safety, bullying or smoking, as well as more formal educational topics.

TIE work is likely to draw upon a wide range of skills, such as playing many different parts, singing, playing musical instruments or helping young people take roles themselves. Actual sessions can vary greatly in length, from short workshops to extended half- or full-day workshops. The touring nature of this work can also mean that it is exhausting – and a driving licence is probably a must.

In some cases teaching experience might be an asset, too – certain TIE companies look for it when recruiting, particularly when their work relates to specific aspects of the National Curriculum. Some companies (such as Oily Cart) also specialise in working with young people who have learning disabilities. You may be expected to attend a special workshop before you can be considered for joining some groups.

TIE can bring great rewards for the actor, and many end up sticking to this field for their whole careers, though if you're hoping for stardom this might not be the route, and rates of pay can be variable. Liking work with young people is of course a prerequisite.

A-Z of TIE companies

ACTIONWORK
{T} 01934 815163
INFO@ACTIONWORK.COM
WWW.ACTIONWORK.COM
Actionwork is one of the South West's leading theatre-in-education companies and performs to schools throughout North Somerset, Somerset, the South West, England, the UK and other parts of the world. Recent international tours included visits to Japan and Malaysia. Through theatre-in-education we can explore many different topics, social issues, and PSHE programmes. All of our shows are backed up with workshops and can include lesson plans, evaluation reports and a variety of other resources.

AESOP'S TOURING THEATRE COMPANY
{T} 01483 724633
INFO@AESOPSTHEATRE.CO.UK
WWW.AESOPSTHEATRE.CO.UK
Aesop's Touring Theatre Company specialises in Theatre in Education, touring schools, art centres and theatres nationally throughout the year with plays and workshops specifically written and designed for Nursery, Infant and Junior age groups. The company aims to educate young audiences through the powers of entertainment and imagination whilst, at the same time, encouraging children to question and think for themselves. A high standard of professionalism is maintained by employing experienced actors with specialist skills and considerable enthusiasm.

ARC
{T} 020 8594 1095
NITA@ARCTHEATRE.COM
WWW.ARCTHEATRE.COM
For more than 20 years Arc has specialised in creating and performing theatre that challenges assumptions and causes real change in the way that people relate to one another at work, at school and in the community. As a pioneering organisation we were instrumental in bringing the issue of racism in football to the forefront of public awareness. The organisations that we work with are those that seek to move forward and achieve a lasting difference, whether it be in the field of diversity, inclusion, education, health, criminal justice or community cohesion.

BARKING DOG
{T} 020 8883 0034
INFO@BARKINGDOG.CO.UK
WWW.BARKINGDOG.CO.UK
Drawing on its vast experience of presenting and devising children's shows and drama, The Barking Dog Theatre company performs at around 250 schools each year. Other venues include: The

Barbican Centre, Cambridge City Festival, The Maltings St Albans, Colchester Arts Centre and many other theatres, arts centres and outdoor events.

BIG WHEEL
{T} 020 7689 8670
WWW.BIGWHEEL.ORG.UK
Big Wheel shows are funny, fresh and focused – which makes them an ideal way to deliver information. We have been presenting schools workshops since 1984. Our tried-and-tested show formats connect with the audience using contemporary pop-culture references and parody. Students have the opportunity to explore sensitive issues and consequences in a safe environment; young people facing challenging decisions and dilemmas are able to share views and consider the facts throughout the show, as well as having a fantastic, memorable time. Big Wheel shows are an example of TIE at its most effective.

BIGFOOT
{T} 0800 6446034
INFO@BIGFOOT-THEATRE.CO.UK
WWW.BIGFOOT-THEATRE.CO.UK
Bigfoot Theatre Company is a UK wide organisation that promotes theatre arts as a tool to educate and empower children and teachers alike. We exist in order to offer quality creative learning experiences that are accessible, sustainable and far reaching.

BITESIZE
{T} 01978 358320
WWW.BITESIZETHEATRE.CO.UK
Bitesize was set up in September 1992 by Artistic Director Linda Griffiths to specialize in theatre for young people. Our aim is to produce high quality, accessible shows for a schools audience and so our annual programme of between ten and twelve productions contains a mixture of shows from new writing to Shakespeare. It includes educational shows based on National Curriculum requirements, adaptations of Classic Stories and entertaining seasonal shows.

BLACK CAT PUPPET THEATRE
{T} 01535 637359
DIANA@BLACKCAT-THEATRE.CO.UK
WWW.BLACKCAT-THEATRE.CO.UK
The Black Cat Theatre company was set up in 1985 and operates from a small village on the edge of the Yorkshire Dales. Founder member Diana Bayliss works as a solo puppeteer/performer, often in collaboration with other artists. The company provides puppet and shadow theatre performances, workshops, residencies and training in schools, theatres and community venues throughout the UK.

BLAH BLAH BLAH!

{T} 0113 2740030

WWW.BLAHS.CO.UK

Based in Leeds for twenty years we have been taking theatre to young people across the country and internationally. Combining creative freedom with stark realism, our plays have provoked, captivated and communicated with hundreds of youth centre and school audiences. The company was created in Leeds in 1985 by three graduates from the Drama, Theatre and Television course at King Alfred's College, Winchester.

BOX CLEVER

{T} 020 7357 0550

ADMIN@BOXCLEVERTHEATRE.COM

WWW.BOXCLEVERTHEATRE.COM

Box Clever is a touring theatre company which performs to over 70,000 young people per year, touring to schools, colleges and theatres across the UK. Our work is broad and contemporary, across many different disciplines including dance, film and music. Led by the writer-in-residence, Michael Wicherek, the company has a particular focus on new writing and creating pathways by which young people become active partici-pants in theatre projects, both within and outside formal education.

BZENTS

{T} 01664 434565

ENQUIRIES@BZENTS.CO.UK

WWW.BZENTS.CO.UK

Bzents specialises in high quality and innovative entertainment for children, families, corporate events, summer fairs and historical events.

C&T

{T} 01905 855436

INFO@CANDT.ORG

WWW.CANDT.ORG

C&T was formed in 1988 by four Drama graduates from University College Worcester (now University of Worcester). Collar and TIE (as the company was then called) soon developed a strong reputation in Worcestershire and the West Midlands for touring plays in the grand tradition of Theatre in Education. Over the last ten years, we have been continuously developing new ideas, placing digital technologies at the heart of the drama, and giving young people a new sense of confidence that drama does connect to their experience, and that they do have a creative contribution to make.

CHAPLINS

{T} 020 8501 2121

ENQUIRES@CHAPLINSPANTOS.CO.UK

WWW.CHAPLINSPANTOS.CO.UK

Touring children's pantomime company, entertaining children of all ages throughout the UK, able to perform in all venues, including schools.

CLASSWORKS THEATRE

{T} 01223 321900

INFO@CLASSWORKS.ORG.UK

WWW.CLASSWORKS.ORG.UK

Classworks was founded in 1983 as Cambridge Youth Theatre by Claudette Bryanston and Jenny Culank to provide a creative outlet for young people aged 15-25 years. The professional touring arm of the company tours at least once per year and is hosted by some of our leading national venues and arts centres, carrying the flag for the best in young people's theatre.

CRAGRATS

{T} 01484 689469

ENQUIRIES@CRAGRATS.COM

WWW.CRAGRATS.COM

As education specialists we design and deliver programmes for schools and other educational environments. We use a range of creative techniques such as theatre roadshows, interactive workshops, media, competitions and awards, special events and much more to make your project powerful and unique. Working with young people is just one element of our service – we connect with teachers, parents and the wider community.

CREW

{T} 0845 260 4414

INFO@CREW.UK.NET

WWW.CREW.UK.NET

Our team are committed to bringing you the very best in educational drama. Promising consistent quality, excitement and learning in over 15 workshops CREW inject drama, humour, and life into all areas of the Primary National Curriculum. With workshops covering Victorians, Romans, healthy living and many more.

DAYLIGHT THEATRE

{T} 01453 733 808

INFO@DAYLIGHTTHEATRE.CO.UK

WWW.DAYLIGHTTHEATRE.CO.UK

DAYLIGHT THEATRE is an independent company presenting up to two hundred performances a year in schools all over Britain and Europe. Their total audience figure is now between one and two million. The company has played at Oxford University, Edinburgh Fringe, Bath International Festival, Bristol Festival for Children and Islington Sixth Form Centre where his Royal Highness, the Prince of Wales attended a special performance of MIND YOUR OWN BUSINESS.

FREEDOM THEATRE
{T} 01225 851651
INFO@FREEDOMTHEATRE.CO.UK
WWW.FREEDOMTHEATRE.CO.UK
Freedom Theatre Company is a professional theatre company and a registered charity based in Bath. The company is committed to excellence and integrity at all levels and is available to bring professional, live theatre to schools, prisons, churches and theatre venues across the region.

FRESHWATER THEATRE
{T} 0844 800 2870
INFO@FRESHWATERTHEATRE.CO.UK
WWW.FRESHWATERTHEATRE.CO.UK
Freshwater Theatre Company is proud to have become one of the most respected theatre-in-education companies in the UK. Over the last ten years the company has brought educational drama to thousands of children in primary and special needs schools all over London and the south east, providing unforgettable entertainment and learning.

GAZEBO
{T} 01902 497222
ADMIN@GAZEOTIE.ORG
Gazebo has been providing inspirational T.I.E. programmes and arts activities for children and young people since 1979. In addition to our core theatre in education programmes, developed to support Every Child Matters, the National Curriculum, and other education initiatives, Gazebo works with community groups, local authorities and regional and national organisations to develop a diverse range of arts and issue based activities. We employ a large number of artists including actors, dancers, musicians, writers, and workshop facilitators to deliver a wealth of projects, working with in excess of 15,000 young people each year.

HALF MOON YOUNG PEOPLE'S THEATRE
{T} 020 7265 8138
ADMIN@HALFMOON.ORG.UK
WWW.HALFMOON.ORG.UK
Half Moon Young People's Theatre aims to produce and present professional theatre for and with young people that informs, challenges and shapes their artistic potential, placing these creative experiences at the core of our policies and practices. The company principally serves London and works exclusively with young people from birth to age 17, placing a particular emphasis upon engaging those often excluded in terms of culture (ethnicity) and ability (disability).

HOBGOBLIN
{T} 0800 5300384
INFO@HOBGOBLINTHEATRECOMPANY.CO.UK
WWW.HOBGOBLINTHEATRECOMPANY.CO.UK
Hobgoblin Theatre Company is a young and dynamic group of actors committed to bringing entertaining, educational theatre into your school. We have all

trained professionally and are members of Equity, as well as having extensive experience of Theatre In Education. We write all of our plays ourselves to ensure that they have a firm historical basis that directly supports the National Curriculum. Each of the hour-long plays brings the past to life through vibrant characters and engaging stories, during which time the children are involved interactively through decision making and discussion.

Hopscotch Theatre Company
{T} 0141 440 2025
INFO@HOPSCOTCHTHEATRE.COM
WWW.HOPSCOTCHTHEATRE.COM
Hopscotch Theatre Company has been entertaining young people in Scotland with fun and educational theatre per-formances for more than 18 years. We tour to primary schools the length and breadth of the country, bringing an enjoyable learning experience to thousands of children each year.

ImpAct Universal Ltd
{T} 01484 660077
GETINTOUCH@IMPACTUNIVERSAL.COM
WWW.IMPACTUNIVERSAL.COM
ImpAct on Learning is a communications and training provider using theatrical techniques. We use drama to help education providers deliver messages, to motivate or challenge students.

Jacolly Puppet Theatre
{T} 01822 852346
THEATRE@JACOLLY-PUPPETS.CO.UK
WWW.JACOLLY-PUPPETS.CO.UK
Jacolly Puppet Theatre is a professional touring company based in Devon, England, which has toured widely on both sides of the Atlantic since 1977. Educational productions are mainly for primary schools and currently include environmental issues, biodiversity, road safety and bullying.

Jack Drum Arts
{T} 01388 765002
INFO@JACKDRUM.CO.UK
Founded in 1986, Jack Drum Arts is one of County Durham's most successful social enterprises. Established as a workers' co-operative, the company delivers a wide range of high quality creative arts programmes across the region and further afield, frequently winning awards for its innovative work. In 2010 the company will finally have a new home, where we aim to establish a digital film and media studio, a costume hire business and a regular programme of drama, music and media activities, with a particular focus on provision for children and young people.

THE KEY STAGE

{T} 01342 892951
INFO@THEKEYSTAGE.CO.UK
WWW.THEKEYSTAGE.CO.UK

The Key Stage is a Theatre in Education company visiting schools across the UK. Our key aim is to make learning fun! Through comedic, exciting and fast-paced theatrical shows, The Key Stage endeavours to both educate and entertain. Every show is accompanied with detailed teachers' notes and suggested educational activities - these can be used in conjunction with the play to enhance the learning experience as a pre or post show lesson.

KINETIC THEATRE

{T} 020 8286 2613
PAUL@KINETICTHEATRE.CO.UK
WWW.KINETICTHEATRE.CO.UK

Kinetic Theatre Company Ltd is a professional Theatre-in-Education company touring musical plays geared to the National Curriculum for Science to Primary schools and theatres throughout the UK. Our purpose is to supplement science teaching practices in a fun, dramatic yet educational way.

KIPPER TIE

KIPPERTIE2004@AOL.COM
WWW.MOLESBUSINESS.COM

Kipper Tie Theatre was formed by writer/director Bernie C. Byrnes and writer/composer Jim Fowler in Newcastle upon Tyne. Our aim is to produce immersive, educational, exciting

and above all entertaining theatre for children of all ages. Our energetic approach, which mixes acting with dance, music and mime, is attracting increasing recognition and has led to our skills being 'loaned out' to companies producing theatre for adults.

LANTERN THEATRE COMPANY

{T} 020 8944 5794
WWW.LANTERNARTS.ORG

Lantern Theatre Company have many shows under their belts and offer a range of performances for different ages and areas of the curriculum. Recent developments have included receiving grants to perform in hospices and hospitals. Lantern Theatre Company enjoys performing in special needs schools and playschemes.

LITTLE FISH

{T} 020 8269 1123
WWW.LITTLEFISHTHEATRE.CO.UK

Our mission is to produce high quality innovative theatre productions and drama experiences for young people in London. Through its activities, the company seeks to challenge social injustice and inspire personal and community growth and change.

LIVE WIRE PRODUCTIONS

{T} 01224 592777
INFO@LIVEWIREPRODUCTIONS.ORG.UK
WWW.LIVEWIREPRODUCTIONS.ORG.UK

Award winning Live Wire Productions, an

ensemble science Theatre in Education company, was founded in 1994 and is a unique resource for schools, the community and organisations seeking to improve an understanding of basic scientific principals as a prerequisite to change in attitudes through drama. All 36 commissioned productions produced by the company to date cover a wide range of subjects where each performance is customised to the group, audience, class etc ensuring that the optimum impact is achieved and that the key messages relevant to the needs of those in attendance are delivered.

LONDON BUS THEATRE
{T} 01208 814514
KATHY@LONDONBUSTHEATRE.CO.UK
WWW.LONDONBUSTHEATRE.CO.UK
The London Bus Theatre Company is one of the leading TIE groups in the UK and can offer schools and colleges drama workshops and DVDs/videos on issues such as bullying, drugs, anti social behaviour and interview techniques. The London Bus Theatre Company converted to a CIC in July 2006 and is one of the leading Theatre in Education groups in the UK. Our funding is from LEAs, community funds and trusts as well as Police Forces and PCTs. We are in constant demand as our work is of the highest quality and has proved to be cost effective for crime and disorder and substance misuse initiatives. BP, the Co operative group and others have sponsored a wide range of projects since 2001.

LOUD MOUTH EDUCATION & TRAINING
{T} 0121 4464880
WWW.LOUDMOUTH.CO.UK
Loud Mouth Educational Theatre Company use theatre to explore young people's issues and views. Our interactive education and training programmes are well researched, lively and accessible, with sessions aimed at adults as well as young people. Loud Mouth tours nationally and internationally and has gained a reputation as one of the country's premier theatre in health education companies.

M6 THEATRE COMPANY
{T} 01706 355 898
INFO@M6THEATRE.CO.UK
WWW.M6THEATRE.CO.UK
M6 Theatre Company is dedicated to the development and presentation of innovative and relevant, high quality theatre for young people. M6 uses theatre as a positive, creative and active learning medium to assist young people's understanding and enrich their imagination.

MAGIC CARPET
{T} 01482 709939
JON@MAGICCARPETTHEATRE.COM
WWW.MAGICCARPETTHEATRE.COM
Magic Carpet Theatre has been presenting shows and workshops since 1982. We tour children's theatre productions and workshops to schools all over the UK and abroad.

MONSTER THEATRE PRODUCTIONS LTD
{T} 0191 2404011
INFO@MONSTERPRODUCTIONS.CO.UK
WWW.MONSTERPRODUCTIONS.CO.UK
Monster is proud to be one of the UK's leading producers of children's theatre for the under sevens and providers of youth theatre programmes. To date we have given literally thousands of children their first experiences of theatre. Using a unique blend of puppetry, performance, interaction and live music we provide young children with an enchanted cornucopia of modern myths and visual magic to appreciate and share with their families.

OILY CART
{T} 020 8672 6329
WWW.OILYCART.ORG.UK
From its beginning in 1981, Oily Cart has challenged accepted definitions of theatre and audience. In particular we have created delightful, multi-sensory, highly interactive productions for the very young and for young people with complex disabilities.

ONATTI
{T} 01926 495220
INFO@ONATTI.CO.UK
WWW.ONATTI.CO.UK
Performs French, Spanish and German language plays for all UK and ROI Secondary Schools and UK primary schools.

THE PLAY HOUSE
{T} 0121 464 5712
INFO@THEPLAYHOUSE.ORG.UK
WWW.THEPLAYHOUSE.ORG.UK
The Play House creates opportunities for children, young people and their families to engage in high quality drama and theatre to explore and make sense of the world they live in. We do this through two touring companies – Language Alive! and Catalyst Theatre – and a range of projects such as The Healthy Living Centre and international projects like For Tomorrow.

PLAYTIME THEATRE
{T} 0)1227 266272
WWW.PLAYTIMETHEATRE.CO.UK
Playtime Theatre Company was established in 1983 with the aim of bringing innovative and entertaining drama to young people in the South of England. Since that time we have established ourselves as one of the leading children's theatre companies, taking our productions to schools and theatres throughout the UK.

POLKA THEATRE
{T} 020 8543 4888
WWW.POLKATHEATRE.COM
Polka Theatre is one of the few venues in the UK which is dedicated exclusively to producing and presenting high quality theatre for young audiences. Since our doors opened in 1979, this unique venue has offered children a first taste of the

thrilling, challenging and inspiring world of theatre. Every year, over 100,000 children discover theatre at Polka.

PROPER JOB

{T} 01484 514 687

MAIL@PROPERJOB.ORG.UK

WWW.PROPERJOB.ORG.UK

Proper Job produces high quality theatre using the biomechanical technique. Our productions tour to community venues including schools and normally include full costume, impressive sets, lighting, music and are fully blacked out to provide a memorable experience for audience and participants. We aim to maximise the full participative potential of performance in theatre through our drama workshops exploring specific issues such as citizenship, local democracy, stereotyping, sex and relationship theatre and substance misuse.

QUANTUM THEATRE

{T} 020 8317 9000

OFFICE@QUANTUMTHEATRE.CO.UK

WWW.QUANTUMTHEATRE.CO.UK

Quantum Theatre for Science was founded in 1988 as a direct response to the lack of educational drama available to schools on the subject of numeracy and science. Over twenty years on, nearly three thousand schools each year see Quantum performances, using them to introduce or re-enforce these topics, making Quantum Britain's foremost science and numeracy-based theatre-in-education company. Our customers have come to rely on Quantum's characteristic style; educational elements combined with pacey, humorous musical theatre. Our aim is to make the world of science and numeracy accessible and relevant to children's everyday experiences by bringing it "to life."

Quicksilver Theatre

talktous@quicksilvertheatre.org

www.quicksilvertheatre.org

Quicksilver Theatre is a children's theatre company who commission and produce new plays and perform them to children the length and breadth of Britain and abroad, providing many with their first experience of live theatre.

SHAKESPEARE 4 KIDZ

{T} 01342 894548

OFFICE@SHAKESPEARE4KIDZ.COM

WWW.SHAKESPEARE4KIDZ.COM

Our unique easy-to-understand musical adaptations of Shakespeare's plays form the basis of a complete understanding of his work. With six plays in our repertoire, S4K is "the ideal introduction to Shakespeare".

SIXTH SENSE

{T} 01793 614864

SSTC@DIRCON.CO.UK

WWW.SIXTHSENSETYP.CO.UK

Sixth Sense is passionate about theatre and young people. Our mission is to produce high quality contemporary theatre that helps young people to fulfill their potential.

SMALL WORLD

{T} 01239 615952

INFO@SMALLWORLD.ORG.UK

WWW.SMALLWORLD.ORG.UK

These are the sorts of things that we do: participatory theatre, arts and culture for development, performances, arts and refugees, workshops, training, puppet and mask making, facilitating participatory consultations, PLA & PRA processes, evaluating arts and development projects, intergenerational projects, processions, carnivals, consultantcy, cabaret, giants and giant shadow puppets, healthy eating and arts projects, multimedia events, installations and more.

SPARE TYRE THEATRE COMPANY

{T} 0207 061 6454

ARTI@SPARETYRE.ORG

WWW.SPARETYRE.ORG

Spare Tyre uses and makes theatre that enables voiceless communities and individuals to share and celebrate their untold stories transforming lives and challenging social prejudice. Spare

Tyre's history of producing bold and powerful theatre that inspires and challenges communities, artists and audiences stretches over thirty years.

TAG THEATRE

{T} 0141 429 0022

INFO@TAG-THEATRE.CO.UK

WWW.CITZ.CO.UK/TAG

TAG Theatre Company is one of the major players in the children and young people's theatre sector in Scotland. TAG continues to offer an exceptionally broad range of highest quality theatre productions and participatory projects designed to engage and inspire Scotland's children and young people. Established in 1967, TAG draws upon unparalleled experience in generating memorable creative experiences for our young citizens both within and outwith the formal education sector. Each year, TAG brings outstanding professional performances to audiences in theatres and schools across the country. All our performance work is supported by fully integrated, cutting edge education programmes.

THEATRE CENTRE

{T} 020 7729 3066

ADMIN@THEATRE-CENTRE.CO.UK

WWW.THEATRE-CENTRE.CO.UK

Theatre Centre exists to commission and present new pieces of professional theatre specifically created for young people. The company was founded in

1953 by Brian Way whose observations of the unimaginative fare offered to children by London theatres led him to explore a more innovative approach.

THEATRE IN EDUCATION TOURS
{T} 01934 815 163
TIE@TIETOURS.COM
WWW.TIETOURS.COM

Tie Tours is an international theatre and training company. We provide shows and workshops to explore many issues including bullying racism and violence. Innovative, exciting, educational and great fun. Established in January 1995, the company has attracted many diverse talented people to its ranks. Exciting shows, amazing workshops: we have performed all over the UK to a variety of people in a variety of venues including schools, youth clubs, community centres, hospitals, open-air housing estates, parks, theatres and festivals.

THRIFT
{T} 01635 41119
OFFICE@THRIFTMUSICTHEATRE.CO.UK
WWW.THRIFTMUSICTHEATRE.CO.UK

Although Thrift root their work in theatre, the emphasis in all of their projects is the learning experience. We try to develop theatre as a medium for developing entrepreneurial activity, teaching young people that experiment is good, certainty does not matter and ways of finding creative solutions to problems. We seek to find ideas for

Theatre in unusual and sometimes difficult places, being inspired by things that most people would never see or notice, anywhere & everywhere. In buildings and architecture; the sounds and rhythms of the street; colours, spaces, people walking past in a hurry.

TRAVELLING LIGHT THEATRE COMPANY
{T} 0) 117 377 3166
INFO@TRAVELLINGLIGHTTHEATRE.ORG.UK

We have been creating theatre for young audiences since 1984. During this time we have created 33 new shows and have become well known for our work for the very young. The company's base is in Bristol and we tour our shows to local schools as well as to theatres and festivals throughout the UK. We also run three thriving youth theatre groups as well as an annual summer school.

Inclusive theatre companies

BIRDS OF PARADISE THEATRE COMPANY

WWW.BIRDSOFPARADISETHEATRE.CO.UK

Birds of Paradise is Scotland's first inclusive touring theatre company working with casts of disabled and non-disabled professional actors.

CHICKENSHED THEATRE

WWW.CHICKENSHED.ORG.UK

Chickenshed is a theatre company. We work using an inclusive creative process which means everyone is welcome, and everyone is valued. Not many places are for everyone and anyone - so a lot of people who find themselves unwelcome elsewhere in the world, come to us. Chickenshed runs Children's and Youth Theatre workshops for 600 people, education courses for over 100 students, community outreach projects and a network of satellite 'Sheds' across the country (and two in Russia) so even more can benefit. Every extraordinary piece of theatre created at Chickenshed shouts out the same thing: anyone can thrive in an environment where everyone is welcome.

DEAFINITELY THEATRE

WWW.DEAFINITELYTHEATRE.CO.UK

Deafinitely Theatre was set up in 2002 by Artistic Director Paula Garfield with Kate Furby and Steven Webb. We are an independent, professional Deaf-led company. Our productions are made from a Deaf perspective and aim to empower Deaf culture, identity and pride locally, nationally and internationally. We create productions in British Sign Language (BSL) and English, which can be understood by everyone and yet retain BSL as the leading language throughout, on and off stage. With a great lack of Deaf Theatre and millions of Deaf people worldwide, we aim to provide a stage for untold Deaf stories, reflecting and exploring Deaf culture by bringing it front stage. Deafinitely Theatre aims to build a bridge between Deaf and hearing worlds by showing plays to both groups as one audience. Our plays set out to correct the misconceptions about the Deaf world – as well as correcting Deaf peoples' mis-conception of the hearing world.

FACE FRONT INCLUSIVE THEATRE

WWW.FACEFRONT.ORG

Face Front has developed a multi-accessible style of performance which is a distinct and exciting theatrical form in its own right, appealing to a wide range of both established and new audiences. The uniqueness of Face Front is that our company includes people with physical, sensory and learning impairments, and those with invisible disabilities and mental health issues, as well as non-disabled people of different ages and ethnic backgrounds.

FREEWHEELERS THEATRE COMPANY

WWW.FREEWHEELERSTHEATRE.CO.UK

The Freewheelers Theatre Company brings disabled and non-disabled actors and supporters, production teams and the local community together. We use theatre and dance, wheelchair and voicebox technology, multimedia, animations, puppets and shadows to create innovative work. We like to work collaboratively, surprise people and challenge perceptions. We don't like barriers, rules or conventions. We welcome new members!

FULL BODY AND THE VOICE

WWW.FULLBODY.ORG.UK

Full Body & the Voice is a successful producing theatre company with a ten year track record in high quality touring productions and co-productions, which reach a broad audience. Our core company of professional learning disabled actors have worked in film, television and theatre at every level. The company works with leading companies, actors, writers and directors and is inclusive in all aspects of it's work. We also deliver high quality corporate training to a range of private, public and voluntary organisations delivering courses on communications and diversity in the workplace and a range of other specialist workshops.

FUNSENSE THEATRE

WWW.FUNSENSETHEATRE.CO.UK

Funsense Theatre is dedicated to providing more accessible theatre for disabled people. Funsense used the term 'disabled people' to include young people with physical visual or hearing impairments, those with learning difficulties, and those who for whatever reason are unable to easily access the world around them. We have based our approach on our own experiences and information provided by disabled young people and their families.

GRAEAE THEATRE COMPANY

WWW.GRAEAE.ORG

Graeae is a disabled-led theatre company that profiles the skills of actors, writers and directors with physical and sensory impairments. Graeae promotes the inclusion of disabled people in professional performance, has developed a unique programme of theatre training and offers writing commissions and training to disabled writers.

HIJINX THEATRE

WWW.HIJINX.ORG.UK

Hijinx Theatre was founded in 1981 by Gaynor Lougher and Richard Berry. The Company's mission statement is to create high quality theatre which is accessible, entertaining and challenging for small communities throughout Wales and England. In the spring and early summer we create a play for adults with learning disabilities and their community. We have created many plays over the years on a variety of pertinent themes, starting from the basic premise that people with learning disabilities experience the same emotional needs as everyone else, but more obstacles are put in their way. We have developed a good working relationship with Mencap Cymru who provide excellent advice about topical issues in the learning disabled community.

IMPACT THEATRE COMPANY

WWW.IMPACTTHEATRE.ORG.UK

Through quality services and training IMPACT uses performing and creative arts to develop skills, increase independence and change attitudes, enabling people with a learning disability to take a more active role within their families and communities.

KALEIDOSCOPE THEATRE COMPANY

WWW.KALEIDOSCOPE-THEATRE.ORG

Kaleidoscope's young thespians have made countless appearances on radio, television and in the press over the years and may have been spotted in A Touch of Frost on the small screen and in Shooting Fish and Titanic Town at the cinema. Kaleidoscope Theatre is a unique company having as it does an integrated cast of players of all ages and from all walks of life. Eight members of Kaleidoscope (six of whom happen to have Down's Syndrome) live and work together all year round in a rambling house in Shropshire and they are joined by friends for rehearsal and performances. Each and every person involved is special. They come because they have a passion for theatre, because they believe in high standards of performance and in quality of life and, above all, because they have a love and high regard for one another.

MIND THE GAP

WWW.MIND-THE-GAP.ORG.UK

Mind the Gap is an experienced touring theatre company based in Bradford, Yorkshire, which performs around the UK and internationally. We are a professional theatre company that helps people with learning disabilities become professional actors, and helps actors with learning disabilities achieve their potential. We don't believe in patronising people, or telling people with learning disabilities what they should aspire to. We do believe in quality theatre productions, raising other people's expectations and we make sure the opportunities we create are accessible to everyone. We know that disabled people and people with learning disabilities come across barriers that can stop them. We also know that many of these barriers can be taken away, or not put in to begin with. That's why we've worked so hard to make our studios, our courses, workshops and website accessible. We want to help challenge people's perceptions of disability-related theatre, and raise expectations of what people with learning disabilities can achieve.

OILY CART

WWW.OILYCART.ORG.UK

Since 1981 Oily Cart has been taking its unique blend of theatre to children and young people in schools and venues across the UK. Challenging accepted definitions of theatre and audience, we create innovative, multi-sensory and highly interactive productions for the very young and for young people with profound and multiple learning disabilities. By transforming everyday environments into colourful, tactile 'wonderlands' we invite our audience to join us in a world of the imagination. Using hydro-therapy pools and trampolines, aromatherapy, video projection, and puppetry together with a vast array of multi-sensory techniques, we create original and highly specialised theatre for our young audiences.

SIGNDANCE COLLECTIVE

HTTP://SITES.GOOGLE.COM/SITE/SIGNDANCECOL-LECTIVE

SDC is lead by Deaf and physically disabled dance theatre artists working alongside composer, musicians. We perform a unique blend of dance, theatre, live music, sign language, and film known as signdance theatre. The

Company travels widely, and incorporates influences from many parts of the world. We bring together deaf and hearing, physically impaired and non-disabled artists, mixing art forms, cultural origins, and abilities to create inclusive, innovative and challenging work.

SPARE TYRE

WWW.SPARETYRE.ORG

Spare Tyre uses and makes theatre that enables voiceless communities and individuals to share and celebrate their untold stories transforming lives and challenging social prejudice. Spare Tyre works intensively with people who have a wide range of disabilities such as dementia, autism, physical and sensory impairments, mental health, downs syndrome, seizures.

TAKING FLIGHT THEATRE COMPANY

WWW.TAKINGFLIGHTTHEATRE.COM

An "exciting and innovative" *professional theatre company that works to break down the barriers which can prevent participation in the arts and creating accessible theatre in exciting venues.

Voiceover work

This chapter was kindly provided by James Bonallack, director of Foreign Voices (www.foreignvoices.co.uk).

How can you succeed in the voiceover business? You've got a brand new voice or showreel with a trendy mix of commercials, corporates and narratives and now you're ready to sit down behind the mic and start earning the big money. Let's start with the good news: if you're Jenny Eclair, Tom Baker or Jack Dee it's easy – your agent calls you, you turn up at the studio where people make a huge fuss of you, you voice a 30-second commercial and then when the cheque arrives you think there's one zero too many on the end. If not, much as with anything else in life, you'll get out what you put in – if you're lucky. Having a great voice is the easy bit – making money with it is a whole different story. This snapshot of the UK voiceover industry will help you make some informed decisions and perhaps avoid some painful mistakes.

Getting started is the most difficult part. People will not be beating a path to your door; you're going to have to get them interested in you and, more importantly, your voice and what you can do with it.

Three golden rules
A producer is looking for three things in a voice. First, that you have a voice that's worth paying for, which means that your voice will have certain qualities. It doesn't mean smooth or rich or sexy or hard sell or sporty or that your voice is recognizable. It doesn't mean that you can narrate or sight read effortlessly for hours. It doesn't even mean that you are studio savvy and know what the engineer wants before he does! It simply means that your voice has got a certain something that he or his client feels fits their requirement which is why your reel has got you a phonecall and which is why you are nervously pacing down a Soho side street looking for a studio with a name like Beach (if they think they're trendy) or Digital Sound and Video Mastering Ltd (if they don't care who thinks they're trendy).

The second thing the producer is expecting is that you do what it says on your demo or voiceover CV. That means if you say you narrate well then you had better be able to narrate well. If it says you're as cheap as chips because you've only done a bit of hospital radio before you decided to become a voice actor then his expectations will be very much less. The point is don't say you're a genius if you're not – you'll be found out!

Finally, the third thing they want from you is that you can take direction. That simply means read what it says on the script unless it's obviously not correct; listen to what you are being asked to do and do it without a fuss and to the best of your abilities. As you gain experience you'll develop confidence about voicing your opinions but to begin with concentrate on getting the right result and showing willing.

Voiceover agents

One of the questions I hear most from new voices is "How do you find a voiceover agent?". Start by sending your demo to agents and anyone else who might be useful – but call first. There is virtually no chance that an agent will take you on if you send your demo in unsolicited. Your chances improve when you take the trouble to ask intelligent questions about their business and how you could be of use to them, supported by a clear voice CV and a short demo with your phone number on the CD and on the box spine.

But do you really need an agent just yet? It sounds odd but actually they are going to be a lot more interested in you if you've got some solid voicing experience under your belt before you start to pester them for representation.

Certainly a good agent will greatly improve your earnings and supply you with regular work but equally there are many voices languishing unused on agency books. I can think of one agency in particular which has 100 or more voices on its books. Their top people work regularly but the rest don't get a look in – the agent is too busy worrying about his star clients. Agencies do hire but they tend to hire by developing relationships with voices they know.

With the advent of online voiceover portals many agencies are booking voices without actually going to the trouble of representing them. The relationship builds and eventually they slot into the agency by default.

(By the way that's a two way street. Many savvy voices are now representing themselves and are represented by more than one agent to find as many outlets as possible for their voice. Having said that, the traditional model of putting all your work via one agent is under threat but still very much in place at the top of the food chain. If you have a top agent you won't want to upset them by touting for work outside of that relationship.)

Internet portals

If you're at all familiar with voiceover portals you'll instantly see the advantages. You're on the internet 24/7; you have your own URL (web address) without having to set up your own site; you can be searched by producers in various ways and you can take advantage of other online databases to send your link to potential clients. The better portals will offer free advice and information about aspects of the industry and directories of relevant contacts. Several portals are very established while the newer ones (www.voicespro.com and www.voicefinder.biz being my two favourites) have highly advanced features and appear much more functional than their older rivals.

Studios are strange places populated by sound engineers who don't see much sunlight. But remember they are your friends. They make you sound good; they help you drop in just after where you inexplicably fluffed for the fifth time and they make you come across as being better than you probably are. Learn the jargon and get a reputation for turning up early and being professional. These are the shortcuts to recommendations and repeat business. The same goes for producers and the money people who pay your invoices – network with anyone who might be useful!

As you develop your skills and find you have a good client base you might want to think about setting up a home studio, perhaps even with an ISDN capability. This is particularly useful for voices that do a lot of radio spots or who live outside London. The advantages are that you are more competitive and can save the production company time by editing your own .wav files. This makes using you convenient and in all probability very good value. The disadvantage is that you could find yourself very isolated as the business is very much one of networking in the pub after the session.

Here it is in a nutshell: be proactive and be professional. The industry is very competitive and luck and timing play a big part.

Stand-up comedy

As a new act in 2001, Hils Barker (**www.hilsbarker.com**) made it to the final of So You Think You're Funny?, Channel 4's national stand-up competition. She went on to co-write groundbreaking sketch show Radio9 for Radio 4 (aired in 2004–2006), and has appeared in and written for BBC TV comedy such as The Message, The Late Edition and The Comic Side of Seven Days. She is also a stand-up on the London and national circuit and here brings advice 'from the coal face'.

People come at stand-up from so many different areas of life it feels presumptuous to describe how to go about it. Why people do it is maybe more interesting. It's got me thinking that being a comedian is not so much a job, more of a condition and it's just a question of when you accept the fact, throw out your social life and start hanging out at clubs called things like 'BrouHaHa' and 'Primrose Hillarity'. I did my first gig at a biker's pub in Islington called the 'Purple Turtle'; it wasn't so much stand-up, more a monologue of five minutes of 'jokes' that I had written, delivered firmly to the back wall and at high speed so no-one could heckle. But I loved it, and after that I was hooked. The first gig raised more questions than it answered: "Where can I do this again?" "How can I do it better?", "Who names these clubs?"

Other questions might be: what are you looking to achieve through doing stand-up, and is it possible to earn a living from it? As hinted above, it's different for everyone. Comics vary so much in style that someone who is perfect for one club may go down terribly in another, and understanding that this doesn't make you crap is really important. Similarly, some comics are live stand-ups through and through; others will want to move into TV and radio, writing or sketch comedy. All of them, though, are probably motivated by having ideas and opinions that they want to 'get out there'.

It's possible to make a great living from stand-up if you're regularly playing all the bigger clubs, such as the Comedy Store, Jongleurs or the Glee, and even if you're not, there are so many clubs at the moment that you can earn a living if you're any good and you gig frequently. Having said that, it can take a good few years to get to either level, because obviously when you start out no-one will pay an inexperienced comedian, and often it costs you money to travel to gigs and do try-out spots for promoters. But as with acting, no-one gets into it because they think it's going to make them any money. You do it for the sheer fun and because you like showing off.

Open mic spots

The first step towards getting started is probably to buy your local listings guide (in London it's Time Out, Glasgow and Edinburgh The List, and so on), get familiar with the comedy section and start turning up at clubs. Go and watch comedy at all levels, from open mic nights to the Comedy Store. It will inspire you, make you laugh, give you an idea of how to shape your material, and also, you start meeting people.

Find out who runs the clubs where you can get yourself a five-minute spot, and either call them or talk to them on the night. In Time Out, you can tell more or less which clubs are for newer acts – they normally have a lot more than the standard three or four comics on the bill, or there'll be a thing saying 'interested acts should call'.

After you've done your first few open spots, I think it's massively encouraging to know that assuming you're in any way funny (and you must be, or you probably wouldn't be interested in doing it in the first place) anything is possible through hard work and fanatical dedication. I use those words advisedly; you can start getting a lot of stage time just by being the one who turns up, and there really will be a lot of new acts who turn up obsessively. I know I did when I started out, and it's true that you don't really make much progress as a comic otherwise. The best way to improve is by turning up at gigs as many nights per week as you can spare, either to get on the bill or just to watch.

It might sound dull but when you really want to play the gigs, nothing works better than a bizarre combination of quasi-stalking tactics and hardcore diary management. (Once you're up and running, with any luck you can get an agent who is brilliant enough to do all that for you.) You could also do one of the various comedy courses on offer.

Good and bad gigs

Don't set too much store by reviews, whether they're negative or positive. There may be reviewers or promoters who think you're shit one minute then brilliant the next, or vice versa. But it's worth reminding yourself that every wonderful comedian who is now a household name or widely accepted as a genius has been through that process, and has had nights where people think they're terrible. As a student at the Edinburgh festival in 1998, I saw one of my favourite stand-ups, a hilarious person, get booed off stage at a gig. I remember mentioning it, shocked, to a stand-up acquaintance, who was starting to do pretty well. His reaction was simply, "And?... Bad gigs happen to everyone."

Up until that point, it just hadn't occurred to me that people probably got better as comedians via a brutal learning curve. I mean, it kind of had, but I'd mainly seen comedy videos and not much of the real live thing. In a way, though, it was liberating to learn that even when you've sort of made it you can still have bad nights. I think it was this piece of knowledge – that comics can watch other comics having a bad gig, but still know that the person on stage is a good comedian – that made me think it might be possible to give stand-up a try.

Agents

It's probably best to wait for an agent to come to you, but you can definitely hurry that along by emailing them and asking them to come and watch you gig, or by entering as many stand-up competitions as possible. There are no rules, though. There are some comics who have been gigging for ten years who don't have or need an agent. If you want to write and perform stuff for TV it can help, but then so can writing material and sending it to script editors and producers at Radio 4 or BBC 7.

It's also worthwhile thinking about what you have as a comic that is unique (remember your personality, which onstage may be a persona, can be just as important as your material, and make audiences buy into weird ideas or even average jokes). If you have long hair and write jokes like Bill Bailey, great, but that major breakthrough may be postponed until Bill Bailey retires. Unless you're a woman, in which case, brilliant; a career as 'the female Bill Bailey' is all set to go.

Also 'as a woman' though, you've got to get used to every reviewer or random person at a party saying, "So, is it hard/different/interesting being a female stand-up?" If you can learn a sarcasm-free answer to that, and the unisex one – "Where do you get your material from?" – and make it look spontaneous every time, you've probably mastered the hardest part. Welcome to the gang…

A-Z of fringe & comedy festivals

This is by no means a comprehensive list of the many arts festivals that take place around Britain and Ireland, but focuses instead on fringe festivals where new productions are likely to be welcomed, as well as events that feature comedy and street theatre. Remember that some of the smaller festivals can come and go over time. It's best to contact organisers a good six months before the actual festival if you're hoping to be involved.

ABERDEEN INTERNATIONAL YOUTH FESTIVAL
WWW.AIYF.OG
INFO@AIFY.ORG
[T] 01224 213800
MONTH: AUGUST
Youth orchestras, choirs, music groups, dance and theatre groups can apply to take part in the festival by sending an application form and a recording of a recent performance. Groups must be of amateur status and made up of people not over the age of 25.

ARTSFEST (BIRMINGHAM)
WWW.ARTSFEST.ORG.UK
ARTSFEST@BIRMINGHAM.GOV.UK
[T] 0121 464 5678
MONTH: SEPTEMBER
The UK's largest free arts festival features strong elements of street theatre and comedy, and potential participants with these skills are invited to make contact via the forms available at the website.

ARUNDEL FESTIVAL FIRNGE
WWW.ARUNDELFESTIVAL.CO.UK
MONTH: AUGUST-SEPTEMBER
Established fringe festival run alongside official Arundel Festival.

ASHBOURNE FESTIVAL
WWW.ASHBOURNEFESTIVAL.ORG
INFO@ASHBOURNEFESTIVAL.ORG
MONTH: JUNE-JULY
Ashbourne Arts and Ashbourne Festival celebrated their tenth anniversary in 2009. The company was granted Charitable status in July 2007 and its primary function is to organise a two-week long Festival during June and July each year. The Festival continues to grow in stature, now attracting support from major funders and internationally known performers to this charming rural area. But not forgetting its community origins, it continues to provide for the cultural needs of the town and surrounding area.

BATH FRINGE FESTIVAL
WWW.BATHFRINGE.CO.UK
ADMIN@BATHFRINGE.CO.UK
MONTH: MAY-JUNE
Over the years the Fringe has investigated and developed artforms events and audiences that have in many cases become mainstream, others of which have been taken on and commercialised by other promoters and festivals. 'Affordable Art',

Spoken Word, Digital Arts & Media, Standup Comedy, Cabaret, Physical Theatre, Circus Arts, Folk & World Music, Latin Dance, Jazz, and the serious presentation of major figures from Pop, Rock and Black Music have all been Fringe centrepieces, some of which have been maintained and others developed elsewhere.

BELFAST FESTIVAL

WWW.BELFASTFESTIVAL.COM
MONTH: OCTOBER-NOVEMBER
Ireland's largest international arts festival, with a plethora of theatre and comedy acts. One of the Festival's enduring key roles is as an advocate of local work, giving Belfast's arts practitioners a unique opportunity to present their work on an international platform.

BEWDLEY FESTIVAL

WWW.BEWDLEYFESTIVAL.ORG.UK
ADMIN@BEWDLEYFESTIVAL.ORG.UK
MONTH: OCTOBER
Festival featuring drama, comedy, music and visual arts, with a range of fringe events.

BRIGHTON FESTIVAL FRINGE

WWW.BRIGHTONFESTIVALFRINGE.ORG.UK
INFO@BRIGHTONFESTIVALFRINGE.ORG.UK
MONTH: MAY
Brighton Festival Fringe is one of the largest and fastest-growing open access arts festival in the world and the largest in England. It sets out to stimulate, educate and entertain a wide audience

by providing a showcase for diverse art forms. No artistic judgment or selection criteria are imposed on participants, enabling the development of both new and established work to attract fresh audiences, press and promoters.

BROUHAHA INTERNATIONAL STREET FESTIVAL (MERSEYSIDE)

WWW.BROUHAHA.UK.COM
INFO@BROUHAHA.UK.COM
MONTH: AUGUST
Brouhaha International is a professional arts organisation that operates within local and international contexts. Our mission is 'To develop and deliver quality arts projects and programmes that meet the needs of children, young people and adults from a range diverse of communities and neighbourhoods at a local, national and international level'.

BURY ST EDMUNDS FRINGE FESTIVAL

WWW.BURYFRINGE.COM
CLAIRE@BURYFRINGE.COM
MONTH: APRIL
With an extensive and varied programme spanning a fortnight of events and shows, hosted by numerous venues throughout the town of Bury St Edmunds, there will be something to involve and appeal to every single member of our community.We are an open-access festival and as such are keen to involve as many people and local groups as possible. Whatever your talent, we will aim to find a place for

you during the Fringe! We're all about the feel-good factor and intend to place a smile firmly on the faces of all those who live, work, study and socialise in our town.

BUXTON FESTIVAL FRINGE

WWW.BUXTONFRINGE.ORG.UK
INFO@BUXTONFRINGE.ORG.UK
MONTH: JULY

Buxton Festival Fringe began in 1980 to run concurrently with the world-renowned Buxton Festival, with international opera and high profile literary talks at its core. The Fringe provides a showcase for performers and artists of all kinds in a variety of venues. Dance, drama, music, poetry, comedy, film, exhibitions and magic are just some of the forms that have appeared - we welcome all genres.

CAMBRIDGE FRINGE FESTIVAL

WWW.CAMFRINGE.COM
INFO@CAMFRINGE.COM
MONTH: JULY-AUGUST

Cambridge Fringe Festival carries on that great tradition of freedom of expression for the arts, by creating a fringe festival that supports an open arts policy with no artistic vetting. For us as organisers it is about bringing you extraordinary performances and emerging talents, often as part of non-commercial shows. It's about that now little used showbiz word "Variety".

CANTERBURY FESTIVAL

WWW.CANTERBURYFESTIVAL.CO.UK
INFO@CANTERBURYFESTIVAL.CO.UK
MONTH: OCTOBER

The Canterbury Festival is Kent's International Arts Festival, the largest festival of arts and culture in the region, and one of the most important cultural events in the South East. The Festival attracts an audience of nearly 80,000 people of all ages to free and ticketed events, drawn from across Kent, London and the South East. With over two hundred events in two weeks there is something to suit everyone from classical music to contemporary dance, and from comedy to world music with theatre, walks, talks, visual arts and much more.

CHELSEA FESTIVAL

WWW.CHELSEAARTSFESTIVAL.ORG
INFO@CHELSEAARTSFESTIVAL.ORG
MONTH: JULY

The chelsea:artsfestival exists to celebrate this unique area and its vital contribution to London's diverse culture; to present the highest quality and distinctive performance; and to ensure that future generations are ever more switched on to all things cultural.

DUBLIN FRINGE FESTIVAL

WWW.FRINGEFEST.COM
INFO@FRINGEFEST.COM
MONTH: SEPTEMBER

A curated fringe festival where artists must apply with examples of previous work.

DUBLIN THEATRE FESTIVAL

WWW.DUBLINTHEATREFESTIVAL.COM
INFO@DUBLINTHEATREFESTIVAL.COM
MONTH: SEPTEMBER-OCTOBER
Our policy is to bring the best available international theatre to Dublin and to balance the programme with Irish productions, especially new plays. The Festival is regarded as the oldest established specialist theatre festival in Europe. Unlike Edinburgh, opera, music and dance do not form a major element of the programme.

THE DYLAN THOMAS FRINGE FESTIVAL

WWW.DYLANTHOMASFRINGE.COM
INFO@DYLANTHOMASFRINGE.COM
MONTH: SEPTEMBER-OCTOBER
The Dylan Thomas Fringe exists to provide a showcase for the best in up and coming talent in the performing arts from Swansea and South West Wales, combined with a range of acts from further afield. Established in 2005, following a successful pilot event the previous year, the Fringe has grown steadily incorporating a wide array of performers and events. Past Fringes have featured Rob Brydon, Harry Hill, Ardal O'Hanlon, Jimmy Carr, James Taylor Quartet, and David McAlmont; alongside a host of eclectic local and national performers.

EDINBURGH FESTIVAL FRINGE

WWW.EDFRINGE.COM
ADMIN@EDFRINGE.COM
MONTH: AUGUST

The Edinburgh Festival Fringe is officially the biggest arts festival in the world, taking place for three weeks in August each year in Scotland's capital city. The event began in 1947 when eight theatre groups turned up uninvited to the first Edinburgh International Festival. The festival caters for everyone from the biggest names in showbiz to the performers in the street and covers all sorts of art forms, such as theatre, comedy, children's shows, dance, physical theatre, musicals, operas, all genres of music, exhibitions, and events.

EXETER SUMMER FESTIVAL

WWW.EXETER.GOV.UK/SUMMERFESTIVAL
GENERAL.FESTIVALS@EXETER.GOV.UK
MONTH: JULY
A festival of music, dance, theatre and comedy.

GRASSINGTON FESTIVAL OF MUSIC AND ARTS

WWW.GRASSINGTON-FESTIVAL.ORG.UK
ARTS@GRASSINGTON-FESTIVAL.ORG.UK
MONTH: JUNE

HEBDEN BRIDGE ART FESTIVAL

WWW.HEBDENBRIDGE.CO.UK/FESTIVAL
MONTH: JUNE-JULY
An annual highlight for the Calder Valley, Hebden Bridge Arts Festival brings the best national and international artists and performers to the area each summer for a celebration of comedy, music, dance, drama, literature and visual arts.

London International Festival Of Theatre (Lift)

WWW.LIFTFESTIVAL.COM

INFO@LIFTFESTIVAL.COM

Established in 1981 by Rose Fenton and Lucy Neal, LIFT, London International Festival of Theatre, has risen to become one of the most important events in the British arts scene, with an influence that reaches far beyond London. Working with artists from across the world to find new ways of seeing the city, LIFT's rich and varied programming has presented extraordinary events in both conventional theatres and in more unusual spaces such as disused power stations, churches and canal basins.

Llangollen Fringe Festival

WWW.LLANGOLLENFRINGE.CO.UK

INFO@LLANGOLLENFRINGE.CO.UK

MONTH: JULY

From its first year in an impromptu tent on an out-of-town playing field through to its present fixed canolfan Town Hall location, via a converted weavers' shed, the Fringe has increased its reputation with every year. Initially the Fringe's mission statement was "to provide entertainment and education to the community of Llangollen, North Wales". This mission has grown with the festival, and now, in addition to offering inspiring, eclectic and high profile events, we actively promote the concept of sustainability - culturally, socially, economically and environmentally.

Manchester International Festival

WWW.MIF.CO.UK

INFO@MIF.CO.UK

MONTH: JUNE-JULY

Manchester International Festival is the world's first festival of original, new work and special events and takes place biennially, in Manchester, UK. The Festival launched in 2007 as an artist-led, commissioning festival presenting new works from across the spectrum of performing arts, music, visual arts and popular culture.

Norwich Fringe Festival

WWW.NORWICHFRINGEFESTIVAL.COM

AMY@NORWICHFRINGEFESTIVAL.COM

MONTH: MAY

The Norwich Fringe Festival aims to bring together all the most exciting arts practitioners in the city. The concept for the Fringe is to redefine the cultural landscape of Norwich over sixteen days of events designed to inform and entertain in equal measure by a loosely knit cabal of leading local arts practitioners, promoters and genuine, home-grown, grass-roots talent.

Oxfringe

OXFRINGE.COM

INFO@OXFRINGE.COM

MONTH: APRIL

Oxfringe began in 2007 with two small literary events, and by 2010 had expanded to more than 200 events across more than 20 venues. It has expanded hugely from its roots as a fringe to the Sunday Times Oxford Literary Festival, and now stands as a festival in its own right, featuring theatre, stand-up comedy, cabaret, jazz, upcoming bands (Radio 2's "Whispering" Bob Harris was the 2010 Oxfringe music patron), dance and street theatre.

PULSE FRINGE FESTIVAL (IPSWICH)

WWW.PULSEFRINGE.COM

MONTH: MAY-JUNE

Showcasing comedy and drama in the East of England.

READING FRINGE FESTIVAL

WWW.MARTINCARR.ORG

MONTH: AUGUST

The Reading Fringe Festival was started in 2005 after a group of musicians decided to put on some events in the week running up to the Carling Reading Festival. This rapidly expanded to become an event that included Art and Dance.

SALISBURY INTERNATIONAL ARTS FESTIVAL

WWW.SALISBURYFESTIVAL.CO.UK

INFO@SALIBSURYFESTIVAL.CO.UK

MONTH: MAY-JUNE

The Festival blazed into life in July 1973. Since then, over a million people have enjoyed outstanding performances of theatre, dance, film and every kind of music, plus literary events and the visual arts. From mid-May to early June each year, the beautiful historic city of

Salisbury is transformed as people flock to the Festival, enjoying both ticketed events and free performances.

SEDBERGH FESTIVAL OF BOOKS AND DRAMA

WWW.SEDBERGH.ORG.UK/BOOKFESTIVAL

WEXFORD FRINGE FESTIVAL

WWW.WEXFORDFRINGE.IE

MONTH: JUNE

Art Exhibitions, Recitals, Dance, Music and specially themed Children's Events

WINDSOR FRINGE

WWW.WINDSORFRINGE.CO.UK

INFO@WINDSORFRINGE.CO.UK

MONTH: SEPTEMBER-OCTOBER

It is the policy of the Fringe to promote fresh talent within the framework of an eclectic programme and many young artists, including jazz performer Jamie Cullum and soprano Dame Emma Kirkby, have cut their teeth in the Fringe and gone on to become household names. The Fringe also likes to promote local talent, and to keep costs as low as possible – so it includes many 'free' events. Over the past few years there have been major developments.

Audition and rehearsal spaces

Aberystwyth

ABERYSTWYTH ARTS CENTRE
ABERYSTWYTH UNIVERSITY
PENGLAIS CAMPUS
ABERYSTWYTH
CEREDIGION SY23 3DE
{T} 01970 622232
JYR@ABER.AC.UK
WWW.ABERYSTWYTHARTSCENTRE.CO.UK/

Birmingham

DANCE XCHANGE
BIRMINGHAM HIPPODROME
THORP STREET
BIRMINGHAM B5 4TB
{T} 0121 689 3170
INFO@DANCEXCHANGE.ORG.UK
WWW.DANCEXCHANGE.ORG.UK

THE MIXING BOWL THEATRE
THE CUSTARD FACTORY
GIBB STREET
BIRMINGHAM B9 4AA
{T} 0121 224 7545
WWW.ROGUEPLAY.CO.UK

REHEARSEALL STUDIO ONE
THE CUSTARD FACTORY
GIBB STREET
BIRMINGHAM B9 4AA
{T} 0121 244 3214
WWW.REHEARSEALL.CO.UK

Brighton

ACADEMY OF CREATIVE TRAINING
8-10 ROCK PLACE
BRIGHTON BN2 1PF
{T} 01273 818266
INFO@ACTBRIGHTON.ORG
WWW.ACTBRIGHTON.ORG

Bristol

CIRCUS MANIACS SCHOOL OF CIRCUS ARTS
43 KINGSWAY AVENUE
KINGSWOOD
BRISTOL BS15 8AN
{T} 0117 947 7042
INFO@CIRCUSMANIACS.COM
WWW.CIRCUSMANIACS.COM

Colchester

SIGNAL MEDIA ARTS THEATRE
VICTORIA CHAMBERS
ST. RUNWALD STREET
COLCHESTER CO1 1HF
{T} 01206 560255
INFO@SIGNALS.ORG.UK
WWW.SIGNALS.ORG.UK

Leamington Spa

THE SPACE UPSTAIRS
C/O HEARTBREAK PRODUCTIONS
{T} 01926 430307

Liverpool

THE BLACK BOX
HUTCHINSON WALK
LIVERPOOL L6 1JW
{T} 0151 260 3000
ADMIN@BLACKBOXMERSEYSIDE.CO.UK
WWW.BLACKBOXMERSEYSIDE.CO.UK

HOPE STREET
13A HOPE STREET
LIVERPOOL L1 9BQ
{T} 0151 708 8007
LAURA@HOPE-STREET.ORG
WWW.HOPE-STREET.ORG

London

THE ACTORS CENTRE
1A TOWER STREET
LONDON WC2H 9NP
{T} 020 7240 3940
OPERATIONS@ACTORSCENTRE.CO.UK
WWW.ACTORSCENTRE.CO.UK

WHITFIELD MEMORIAL CHURCH
79A TOTTENHAM COURT ROAD
LONDON W1P 9HB
{T} 020 7580 2791
WWW.AMCHURCH.CO.UK/LATCHCOURT.HTM

NEW DIORAMA THEATRE
15-16 TRITON STREET
REGENT'S PLACE
LONDON NW1 3BF
{T} 020 7916 5467
GUYHOLLANDS@QUICKSILVERTHEATRE.ORG
WWW.NEWDIORAMA.COM/

JERMYN STREET THEATRE
16B JERMYN STREET
LONDON SW1Y 6ST
{T} 020 7434 1443
INFO@JERMYNSTREETTHEATRE.CO.UK
WWW.JERMYNSTREETTHEATRE.CO.UK/HIRE.HTML

MENIER CHOCOLATE FACTORY
53 SOUTHWARK STREET
LONDON SE1 1RU
{T} 020 7378 1712
OFFICE@MENIERCHOCOLATEFACTORY.COM
WWW.MENIERCHOCOLATEFACTORY.COM/PAGES/RE
HEARSAL_ROOM_PRIVATE_HIRE

PINEAPPLE DANCE STUDIOS
7 LANGLEY STREET
COVENT GARDEN
LONDON WC2H 9JA
{T} 020 7836 4004
LAURA@PINEAPPLE.UK.COM
WWW.PINEAPPLE.UK.COM/STUDIO_HIRE/DEFAULT.ASPX

DANCE WORKS
16 BALDERTON STREET
LONDON W1K 6TN
{T} 020 7318 4100
INFO@DANCEWORKS.NET
WWW.DANCEWORKS.NET/STUDIO-HIRE

CAMDEN PEOPLE'S THEATRE

58-60 HAMPSTEAD ROAD
LONDON NW1 2PY
{T} 020 7419 4841
ADMIN@CPTHEATRE.CO.UK
HTTP://CPTHEATRE.CO.UK/HIRE.PHP

SPOTLIGHT STUDIOS

1ST FLOOR, SPOTLIGHT
7 LEICESTER PLACE
LONDON WC2H 7RJ
{T} 020 7440 5041
THOM.HAMMOND@SPOTLIGHT.COM
WWW.SPOTLIGHT.COM/STUDIOS/INDEX.HTML

THE DRILL HALL

16 CHENIES STREET
LONDON WC1E 7EX
{T} 020 7307 5060
BOX.OFFICE@DRILLHALL.CO.UK
WWW.DRILLHALL.CO.UK/P12.HTML

CHELSEA THEATRE

WORLD'S END PLACE
KINGS ROAD
LONDON SW10 0DR
{T} 020 7349 7811
ADMIN@CHELSEATHEATRE.ORG.UK
WWW.CHELSEATHEATRE.ORG.UK

CASTING STUDIOS

RAMILLIES HOUSE
1-2 RAMILLIES STREET
LONDON W1F 7LN
{T} 020 7437 2070
INFO@CASTINGSTUDIOS.COM
WWW.CASTINGSTUDIOS.COM/CASTING_FACILITIES.PHP

LONDON REHEARSAL ROOMS (LONDON SCHOOL OF MUSICAL THEATRE)

83 BOROUGH ROAD
LONDON SE1 1DN
{T} 020 7407 4455
LAURA@LSMT.CO.UK
WWW.LONDONREHEARSALROOMS.COM/INDEX.HTM

THE OCTOBER GALLERY

24 OLD GLOUCESTER STREET
BLOOMSBURY
LONDON WC1N 3AL
{T} 0207 831 1618
RENTALS@OCTOBERGALLERY.CO.UK
WWW.OCTOBERGALLERY.CO.UK/ABOUT_US/SPACES.SHTML

ANTENNA STUDIOS

BOWYERS YARD
BEDWARDINE ROAD
CRYSTAL PALACE
LONDON SE19 3AN
{T} 020 8653 5200
INFO@ANTENNASTUDIOS.CO.UK
WWW.ANTENNASTUDIOS.CO.UK/REHEARSAL

THE FUTURE GALLERY

5 GREAT NEWPORT STREET
LONDON WC2H 7HY
{T} 020 3301 4727
INFO@FUTUREGALLERY.CO.UK
WWW.FUTUREGALLERY.CO.UK/HIREUS

CASTING AS SWEET
SWEET ENTERTAINMENTS LTD
42 THEOBALD'S ROAD
LONDON WC1X 8NW
{T} 020 7404 6411
INFO@SWEET-UK.NET
WWW.SWEET-UK.NET/CASTING/INDEX.HTM

PAINES PLOUGH 'BIG ROOM'
PAINES PLOUGH THEATRE COMPANY
4TH FLOOR
43 ALDWYCH
LONDON WC2B 4DN
{T} 020 7240 4533
OFFICE@PAINESPLOUGH.COM
WWW.PAINESPLOUGH.COM/CMS/INDEX.PHP?ID=4

BIG CITY STUDIOS
MONTGOMERY HOUSE
159-161 BALLS POND ROAD
ISLINGTON,
LONDON N1 4BG
{T} 020 7241 6601
PINEAPPLE.AGENCY@BTCONNECT.COM
WWW.PINEAPPLEAGENCY.COM/BIGCITY.PHP

ISLINGTON ARTS FACTORY
2 PARKHURST ROAD
HOLLOWAY
LONDON N7 0SF
{T} 020 7607 0561
INFO@ISLINGTONARTSFACTORY.ORG
WWW.ISLINGTONARTSFACTORY.ORG/FACILITIES

OUT OF JOINT
7 THANE WORKS
THANE VILLAS
LONDON N7 7NU
{T} 020 7609 0207
OJO@OUTOFJOINT.CO.UK
WWW.OUTOFJOINT.CO.UK/ABOUTUS/REHROOM.HTML

JACKSON'S LANE
269A ARCHWAY ROAD
HIGHGATE
LONDON N6 5AA
{T} 020 8340 5226
JENNI@JACKSONSLANE.ORG.UK
HTTP://WWW.JACKSONSLANE.ORG.UK/#/38

BALLY STUDIOS
UNIT 16 MILLMEAD BUSINESS CENTRE
MILLMEAD ROAD
TOTTENHAM HALE
LONDON N17 9QU
{T} 020 8808 0472
INFO@BALLYSTUDIOS.CO.UK
WWW.BALLYSTUDIOS.CO.UK/HOME.HTM

THE FACTORY FITNESS AND DANCE CENTRE
407 HORNSEY ROAD
LONDON N19 4DX
{T} 020 7272 1122
INFO@FACTORYLONDON.COM
WWW.FACTORYREHEARSALSTUDIOS.COM

SEVEN SISTERS STUDIO (ZEITGEIST THEATRE COMPANY)
5 FOUNTAYNE ROAD
SEVEN SISTERS
LONDON N15 4QL
{T} 07989 405 385
ZIA@ZEITGEISTTHEATRE.COM
WWW.ZEITGEISTTHEATRE.COM/INDEX.HTM

BEYOND CENTRE
21 STONEHOUSE
EADE ROAD DESIGN CENTRE
199 EADE ROAD
LONDON N4 1DN
{T} 07921 950 704 / 07886 984 526
MIRIAM@BEYOND-CENTRE.COM / AMY@BEYOND-CENTRE.COM
WWW.BEYOND-CENTRE.COM/INDEX.HTML

3 MILLS STUDIOS
THREE MILL LANE
LONDON E3 3DU
{T} 020 7363 3336
INFO@3MILLS.COM
WWW.3MILLS.COM

TOYNBEE STUDIOS
28 COMMERCIAL STREET
LONDON E1 6AB
{T} 020 7247 5102
ADMIN@ARTSADMIN.CO.UK
WWW.ARTSADMIN.CO.UK/TOYNBEESTUDIOS

AVIV DANCE STUDIOS
WATFORD BOYS GRAMMAR SCHOOL
RICKMANSWORTH ROAD
WATFORD WD18 7JF
{T} 01923 250 000
VIA WEBSITE
WWW.AVIVDANCE.COM/INDEX.PHP

THE SPACE
269 WEST FERRY ROAD
LONDON E14 3RS
{T} 020 7515 7799
INFO@SPACE.ORG.UK
HTTP://SPACE.ORG.UK/?PAGE_ID=49

THE RAG FACTORY
16-18 HENEAGE STREET
LONDON E1 5LJ
{T} 020 7650 8749
HELLO@RAGFACTORY.ORG.UK
WWW.RAGFACTORY.ORG.UK/REHEARSALSPACE.HTM

STUDIO 1-ON-1
HEADNOD TALENT AGENCY
63 REDCHURCH STREET
BETHNAL GREEN
LONDON E2 7DJ
{T} 020 7502 9478
STUDIO1ON1@HEADNODAGENCY.COM
WWW.HEADNODAGENCY.COM/HEADNOD_STUDIO.HTML

STAGE WORKS PRODUCTIONS
{T} 020 8525 0111
INFO@STAGEWORKSPRODUCTIONS.CO.UK
WWW.STAGEWORKSPRODUCTIONS.CO.UK/MAINMENU.HTML

The Amadeus Centre
50 Shirland Road
Little Venice
London W9 2JA
{T} 020 7286 1686
INFO@AMADEUSCENTRE.CO.UK
WWW.AMADEUSCENTRE.CO.UK/MUSIC.HTML

Rambert Dance Company
94 Chiswick High Road
London W4 1SH
{T} 020 8630 0601
RDC@RAMBERT.ORG.UK
WWW.RAMBERT.ORG.UK/STUDIO_HIRE

The Kings Head
214 High Street
Action
London W3 9NX
{T} 020 8993 3595
TOMAS@CARPE-NOCTEMENTERPRISES.CO.UK
WWW.KINGSHEADACTION.COM

London Bubble Theatre Company
5 Elephant Lane
London SE16 4JD
{T} 020 7237 4434
ADMIN@LONDONBUBBLE.ORG.UK
WWW.LONDONBUBBLE.ORG.UK/HIRE_STUFF

Battersea Arts Centre (BAC)
Lavender Hill
Battersea
London, SW11 5TN
{T} 020 7326 8211
VIA WEBSITE
WWW.BAC.ORG.UK/HIRES

Brixton Community Base
Talma Road
London SW2 1AS
{T} 020 7326 4417 / 07958 448 690
CAROFUNNELL@BSVCC.ORG
WWW.BSVCC.ORG/SPACE.HTML

Arch 468
Unit 4
209A Coldharbour Lane
London SW9 8RU
{T} 07973 302 908
VIA WEBSITE
WWW.ARCH468.COM/REHEARSAL_SPACE_HIRE.HTML

Jerwood Space
171 Union Street
London SE1 0LN
{T} 020 7654 0171
SPACE@JERWOODSPACE.CO.UK
WWW.JERWOODSPACE.CO.UK/INDEX.HTML

Watermans
40 High Street
Brentford TW8 0DS
{T} 020 8232 1019
MIRKO@WATERMANS.ORG.UK /
EDOARDO@WATERMANS.ORG.UK
WWW.WATERMANS.ORG.UK/ABOUT/FOR_HIRE

Creekside Studios
Units C102 & C104
Faircharm Trading Estate
8-12 Creekside
London SE8 3DX
{T} 020 8694 9484

INFO@CREEKSIDESTUDIOS.CO.UK
WWW.CREEKSIDESTUDIOS.CO.UK/REHERSAL.HTML

INTERMISSION
WALTON PLACE
LONDON SW3 1SA
{T} 020 7589 5747
AMANDA@INTERMISSION.ORG.UK
HTTP://WWW.INTERMISSION.ORG.UK/

ST GABRIEL'S HALLS
GLASGOW TERRACE
CHURCHILL GARDENS
PIMLICO
LONDON SW1V 3AA
{T} 07967 655515
INFO@STGABRIELSHALLS.ORG.UK
WWW.STGABRIELSHALLS.ORG.UK

STUDIO SEVENTEEN
UNIT 17
ZENNOR ROAD
BALHAM
LONDON SW12 0PS
{T} 020 8675 6708 / 07762 541089
INFO@STUDIO-SEVENTEEN.CO.UK
STUDIO-SEVENTEEN.CO.UK

Manchester

PHA (MANCHESTER)
TANZARO HOUSE,
ARDWICK GREEN NORTH
MANCHESTER M12 6FZ
{T} 0161 273 4444
INFO@PHA-AGENCY.CO.UK
WWW.PHA-AGENCY.CO.UK

WATERSIDE ARTS CENTRE
WATERSIDE PLAZA
SALE M33 7ZF
{T} 0161 912 5898
LOUISE.BURGESS@TRAFFORD.GOV.UK
WWW.WATERSIDEARTSCENTRE.CO.UK

Stafford

STAFFORD GATEHOUSE THEATRE
EASTGATE STREET
STAFFORD ST16 2LT
{T} 01785 253595
GATEHOUSE@STAFFORDBC.GOV.UK
WWW.STAFFORDGATEHOUSETHEATRE.CO.UK

Warrington

EUROKIDS & ADULTS AGENCY CASTING STUDIOS
THE WAREHOUSE STUDIOS
GLAZIERS LANE
CULCHETH
WARRINGTON WA3 4AQ
{T} 0871 222 7470
ADMISSIONS@EKA-AGENCY.CO.UK
WWW.EKA-AGENCY.CO.UK

Section 5
Living as
an actor

The business of you

Marketing yourself
Hopefully by now you have a basic grounding in creating your main self-marketing kit: CV, photograph and show/voicereel. You may choose to register with an Online Casting Service. What else can you do? Always be on the lookout for opportunities to promote yourself. This doesn't mean being overconfident or excessively pushy – rather, get talking to people, make connections, show an interest, and give people reasons to want to talk to you again. If you're looking for work in the corporate field, consider getting business cards and a letterhead printed. Remember that people take you according to how you present yourself – try to talk to them in their 'language'.

Part of being professional is being organised, too. Make sure it's easy for people to get in touch with you – phone, email – and don't give them reasons to think less of you, such as a silly outgoing ansaphone message. Keep track of your appointments and make sure you're always on time for them. Keep a record of people in the industry that you've met and their contact details, and maybe even a diary of performances you've seen – it all helps you to feel part of something, and you never know when a name in a file might be just the connection you need to help you get work.

Beating the blues
Everyone knows the clichés about actors working in fast-food outlets when they're 'between jobs'. Hopefully this book will have given you some solid guidance to get more rewarding work than that, but if not, never despair, and always come back fighting when you've been turned down for something.

Beyond applying for acting jobs, make sure you go and see other productions, too: seeing a really good performance or production can lift your spirits and remind you just why you're in this business! Also, it's important to take time out and enjoy yourself, however well or badly work is going. Your general well-being is vital and will make you more resilient in the face of disappointment, not to mention more dynamic as a performer. Keep yourself fit and healthy: eat well, and get plenty of exercise. Doing classes such as pilates or yoga can help here, or join a gym, or simply go swimming, cycling or running regularly. All this will help you keep your body in tone, which will show in your work. We don't want to sound like your mother here, but these things really count. Time after time studies show it's things like this that keep people happy rather than making pots of cash – not that the latter wouldn't help now and then.

Acting is a unique job that brings happiness to thousands of audiences every year, and the more positive you are in the gaps between work, the more you'll be part of a 'feedback loop' that keeps you buoyant too, and at the peak of your performance.

Defying gravity
Keeping the faith in an actor's ever changing reality

By Keisha Amponsa Banson, a recent graduate of Mountview Academy of Theatre Arts, London.

Well, at least that's what it feels like on stage when you're belting out Broadway hits or giving your Hamlet at the RSC. Surviving in this ever competitive industry on the other hand is another matter entirely. It's often an uphill struggle against constant rejection, a thorough mauling by the critics, unemployment, looming financial ruin and a slew of unsuccessful castings (melodramatic? I think not). And yet why do we keep coming back for more? My mini guide should at least take the edge off some of the daunting tasks ahead like finding an agent, attending auditions and choosing drama schools to keeping abreast of the latest news in the acting world, which, more often than not keeps a savvy performer in work.

I had my first true taste of fame when I was a finalist on BBC One's I'd Do Anything, Andrew Lloyd Webber's TV talent search for Nancy in the musical Oliver! I was thrown in at the deep end and though I enjoyed myself immensely and the experience was invaluable, I admit that I was perhaps a little overwhelmed by my peers on a reality TV show, where most of the girls had either trained or were West End veterans. I realised very quickly that though I loved the competitive hustle of show business, to last in a trade which is traditionally so cutthroat, I was going to have to hone my talents in a more conventional setting – drama school.

I was blessed enough to get into the only drama college I applied for but this will obviously not be the case for all. Research carefully and choose wisely, after all, this could arguably be the school that you'll be spending the next three years at. Ask yourself does LAMDA have individual singing lessons? Do RADA do stage combat? Does GSA have acting for camera and audition technique? Visit the campuses and get in touch with course administrators and alumni to get a real sense of each institution. Drama school is also very expensive and so looking into grants, trusts, Career Development Loans and other scholarships on offer at the academies or researching online are all important before applying.

I went to drama school because I knew there were specific skills I lacked and needed a while away from the spotlight to gain confidence as a performer, but not everyone is the same. If drama school is not your thing, individual tuition/acting, singing and dance lessons are often advertised in publications like The Stage newspaper (**www.thestage.co.uk**) or at establishments such as The Actor's Centre (**www.actorscentre.co.uk**) in London, a brilliant resource and a chance to find classes or one-on-one tuition where you can be taught by the UK's top acting coaches who work in TV, theatre and film. On the other hand, if drama school is up your street, then get cracking!

So you've decided to go (or not to go – sorry, I couldn't resist!) to drama college and you've gotten to the point in your burgeoning career that you need representation, i.e. an agent to make castings and getting work that little bit easier. One of the obvious perks of going to drama school is the opportunity for showcases and final performances of musicals and plays for you to invite the casting elite to see you strut your stuff. Not all will get agents clamouring for you after graduation so getting people to see you in either a cabaret concert or an am-dram production of Romeo and Juliet is often the only way of enticing agents and casting directors to take the bait, take a chance on an unknown but exciting actor and take you on their books or cast you in their new play. There are other options though. Armed with your copy of Contacts (**www.contactshand-**

book.com), make a list of approximately ten to fifteen agents that you'd like to represent you. Don't be drawn only to the bigger agents but at the same time don't settle for an agent who doesn't see eye to eye with you about your castability, who may not market you to the right casting directors and could ultimately have limited contacts in the industry.

Another great resource is Spotlight (**www.spotlight.com**). Make sure you become a member of this great casting service. One of my favourite past times (so sad but true...) is to type in the name of a UK actor I admire into Spotlight's mini search engine and discover who they're represented by. It's a very useful tool if you don't know where to start in regards to good agents. With agent list in hand, get some black and white 10 x 8 headshots sorted (though colour is being used more frequently now) and printed/Repro'd along with a covering letter and CV and send out a mass mailing to as many agents as possible. You may get a response from several agents, from a few or none at all but take heart! You aren't the first actor to be so resoundingly rejected and you surely won't be the last. Whether you get an agent or not, it's good to keep your ears to the ground about future castings and try to get to any open auditions or chat to your agent about being seen for specific roles, shows and casting teams. Knowing your castability as a performer is crucial. Being seen for Lady Macbeth when you're so obviously an Ophelia would perhaps be slightly frustrating but ultimately the challenge of exploring new characters is all part of the thrill of being an actor.

"I'm not getting the work and the bills are piling up", I hear you cry. Fear not! It's so easy to get downhearted in this career you've chosen but establishing an almost foolhardy optimism and resilience is vital to surviving in this competitive market. Keep busy. Join the gym or take up yoga, Pilates, hip hop, salsa or tap dancing. Keeping healthy is all part of being an actor so don't get complacent. Find a job working Front of House or Box Office at a theatre. Find acting work for yourself (some agencies operate in this way so you may already be doing this). Get networking on Facebook, MySpace, Twitter, Bebo and other social networking sites (though good old fashioned networking parties are generally twice as glamorous and just as rewarding).

Staying active should help to drive those jobbing actor blues away but make sure you meet people outside of the industry as well – it certainly keeps me sane. Stop complaining about life and live it. Do this so you're able to steal bits here and there like a gleeful magpie and use in your work. You're a detective of human behaviour so glean as much as you can from your friends' marriages, pregnancy scares, fashion disasters and bad hair days. You have to be seen as the one in the audition with the tenacity, audacity and pugnacity to get that role and deliver a fearless performance, so a little eavesdropping on a conversation you overheard on the Tube could be the difference between the role of a lifetime and the checkout at Tesco's.

Like it or not, you have become a marketable commodity and it's your job to sell your brand name. Even though it quite often is the luck of the draw when you are selected or rejected for a prospective job, there are plenty of other things you can do to help yourself along. Remembering that you are your own unique variety of fabulousness should help you cultivate an aura of self assuredness in your talent and the flair and originality by which you express it. Picking up new skills along the way like learning a new instrument or a new language are more strings to your bow and help open up new avenues for castings.

Create a website promoting your past, present and future projects, write your own musical or screenplay, get a show and voicereel sorted and send out DVDs/CDs of yourself to casting directors to get you seen for commercials, TV and film. See films, plays and watch the latest TV dramas to keep up-to-date with new faces in the industry. Go to every function armed with your Little Black Book (or BlackBerry) to hand to take down those important contact details that you can't afford to forget. Develop the memory of an elephant. Random, I know, but it can help in any situation from learning lines to remembering the face of a director you worked with 10 years ago. Finally, try really hard to receive constructive criticism from family, friends, other actors/directors and the critics. It's truly humbling to hear the brutal honest truth from loved ones and I often have to laugh at how way off or pitch perfect their views on my performance can be. Above all, keep the faith and don't lose your passion for the noble profession even when you're constantly turned down. It's not the end of civilisation if you do - you could always be a lawyerJ.

Last, but by no means least, keep those receipts! Good luck and God Bless!

Tax and accounting

Naturally as an actor your focus is always going to be on your performances – that's why you're doing all this! But it's important to remember that you are also running a business. As with any self-employed person (unless you're lucky enough to have a full-time job with a theatre company you respect), whether a freelance writer, a plumber or a taxi driver, this means that there is background admin to be done, as well as the business of promoting yourself.

When you start out, acting may only take up a smallish proportion of your time, and you might have a 'day job' of some kind to tide you over – but income you make as an actor often (but not always – see below) counts as self-employment, and of course you will need to make time for applying for more acting work. In this chapter we'll provide a quick survey of some of the main issues which you should consider.

Self-employment
When you 'go it alone', it's not just a question of finding the work and banking the money: you still need to pay tax, for one thing. From a tax point of view, you may well be both employed and self-employed – it depends partly on how you are paid. In some cases you may find your tax is paid at source (PAYE) before you get the money, and historically the Inland Revenue has been keen to see 'entertainers' as a special case to be treated as employees – it means you can claim fewer expenses.

Now that self-assessment is well-established, however, it's quite likely that work where your tax isn't deducted at source will be regarded as self-employment. The most important thing to do is talk to HM Revenue & Customs – their telephone helpline staff are helpful and not at all like the intimidating 'taxman' of old.

The HMRC website also has loads of advice on this subject: see www.hmrc.gov.uk/employment-status/ for a starting point. In the section under 'special cases', you'll find that it says "entertainers who are not employed under a contract of service or in an office with emoluments chargeable to tax... as employment income are treated as employed earners provided their remuneration consists wholly or mainly of salary. If it does not, they retain their self-employed status."

If the Revenue sends you a self-assessment form (for declaring income in a particular tax year, ie 6 April in one calendar year to 5 April in the next), you may need then to fill out sections both for 'employment' and for 'self-employment'. These need to be submitted by the end of the January after the tax year in question (though that's changing to the earlier time of September in the next year or two).

Payment (for any tax not taken at source) is made in two halves in January and July 'on account' for the following tax year. As well as tax, you will need to pay National Insurance. Remember: there are fines for being late with payments. The Revenue is currently encouraging people to use its online submission service rather than the traditional paper format.

All this can get very confusing. There's a simple solution: go and see an accountant! Also, if you're a member of Equity, get hold of its 'Advice and Rights Guide' for reference.

Accountants

The most important thing is to keep records of your work and income, and the relevant dates. You don't have to become obsessed with double-entry bookkeeping (though it could help) – but keep a clear record of income and outgoings related to work. This means invoices, payslips, details of cheques, and receipts for anything work-related. In terms of the latter, promotional items such as photographs and showreels ought to be tax deductable as expenses – if you're self-employed. Don't take our word for it, however: get an accountant.

Accountants are experts at things like expenses and will almost always think of things that wouldn't occur to you however much you might have read up on the subject. You can find a list of accountants specialising in finances for actors at the end of this chapter.

As a general rule, using the services of an accountant will pay for itself: having your tax return prepared will probably cost in the region of £300, but they can usually save you that and more on tax deductable expenses. Many accountants will invite you for a free initial meeting to discuss your affairs, and you can take things from there. Take any correspondence from the Revenue with you, and details of income and outgoings.

Other finances

Given the precarious lifestyle you've chosen, it's wise to bone up on other financial issues. Do you want to take out a mortgage to buy a home, for example? It's perfectly possible, and these days lenders are much less prejudiced about the self-employed than they used to be. Nevertheless, they will want to see recent accounts, perhaps for the last three years, and several months' worth of bank statements. Make sure you have all this information well organised.

Even if you're only renting a property, letting agents are getting increasingly stern about checking up on this stuff. Often they expect a 'guarantor' (someone who will cover the payments if you default), such as a parent, even for tenants well into adult life. If you have someone suitable to cover you like this, make sure you speak to them beforehand!

Another dirty word to people in creative fields is 'pensions'. You might be young and care-free now, but how will you sustain yourself in old age (assuming you don't become the next Inspector Morse)? It's worth thinking about how to save now to avoid a crisis later on. For all of these issues, you're best off talking to an expert again. Check out www.unbiased.co.uk to track down an independent financial adviser (IFA) in your area.

Accounting FAQs

Content supplied by TWD Accountants. With over 30 years experience in practice, TWD Accountants is one of the UK's leading low cost, fixed fee tax accountancy services. TWD provide advice and guidelines to help actors and sole traders find their way through the UK tax maze.

'I have just become an actor - what expenses can I claim against my tax?'

There are many expenses that can be claimed against taxable income. Everyone runs their business in a different way and they will usually incur some expenditure that is particular to them. By law you can only claim expenses that are incurred Wholly and Exclusively for business purposes.

So items that are exclusively related to your self employment should be allowed e.g. advertising, accountancy fee, agent fees/commission etc

However many expenses may have a 'dual purpose,' i.e., they will have a business and a personal element and as a general rule you can only claim the business proportion of such items providing you can ascertain a business element.

The following list is not exhaustive but gives an indication of the general expenses that may be claimed by an Actor depending on the individual circumstances of the claim:

- Agent / Manager fees and commission
- Travel & subsistence on tour if supporting a permanent home
- Costume & Props
- Laundry & cleaning of costume & props
- Travelling and expenses attending interviews and auditions
- Postage & stationary.
- Computer consumables.
- Bank charges on a business account.
- Telephone/mobile phone charges.

- Accountancy charges.
- Equity subscriptions
- Advertising e.g. Spotlight and agency books
- Theatre and cinema tickets relevant to your self-employment

If you have expenses that are not on this list you may still be able to claim them.

Keep a full record of ALL expenses and discuss them with your accountant. They may be tax deductible.

'I have recently had cosmetic surgery - can I include these costs in my accounts?'

Unfortunately, the answer is probably not.

Only in exceptional circumstances will non health related operations to change personal appearance by reversing or masking the ageing process not have a private purpose.

If the purpose to change your appearance was to gratify a private wish to improve / change your appearance then no deduction will be due. However, some performers are able to show that expenditure has been incurred solely for professional purposes.

One example is a radio performer who start to do TV work. She is advised that her irregular teeth are holding back her TV work so she has cosmetic surgery to correct this. It was established with HMRC that as she was previously satisfied with her appearance then the TV work was the sole reason for the dentistry and they allowed the cost.

'I am worried that my bookkeeping records would not stand up to a tax investigation - what records should I be keeping?'

You should keep comprehensive records with supporting receipts.

Anyone who has undergone an investigation will know that HM

Revenue & Customs can spend months looking through your records, asking probing questions and wanting what might seem as meaningless information about your business affairs. This can be both time consuming, stressful and very expensive – not just in terms of tax but in terms of your own lost time spent dealing with any investigation.

Prevention is of course better than cure.

One recommendation is to have a separate business bank account. If a credit card is preferable, then again, separating business and personal transactions into two separate cards could be helpful.

Separating your business and personal life will not only help your accountant but it will also help in the event of an HMRC investigation.

There are three general forms of transaction to record:

• Bank transactions, including payments from and deposits into the bank.
• Cash payments and receipts
• Credit card payments

When deciding on how to record these transactions provision should be made to identify which receipts / payments are cash, bank or credit card. For cash receipts, it is important to identify any cash not deposited in the bank but used for sundry cash expenses or general living expenses.

Personal drawings from the business should also be easily identified. One area HMRC looks at is funding of personal expenses. If you have separate business and private accounts, either make transfers between accounts or write yourself a cheque from the business account.

Mileage records are also important. Even if you use your car almost exclusively for business some form of record should be kept to validate this. HMRC are keen to challenge business mileage where records are not complete.

Given that a proportion of your mileage will be business related, one method is to record your car's total mileage at the start of your accounting year and only record your private journeys made during the year. At the end of the accounting year, work out the total mileage and deduct the private mileage. The difference is your business miles.

If you do not have sufficient evidence to support your business expenses then an investigation can mean an increased tax bill. HMRC may also make similar adjustments to the previous year's tax bills, add on interest charges and impose penalties.

Please also bear in mind that bookkeeping records and supporting receipts should be retained for 5 year 9 months after being submitted to HMRC.

'I have just bought some new clothes for work - can I put this cost through my accounts?'

Possibly.

The general rule for clothing is that a self employed person cannot claim a deduction for the cost of 'a wardrobe of everyday'. However, the cost of clothing acquired for a film, stage or TV performance is allowable. This clothing is not regarded as 'everyday wardrobe'; it is a 'costume' used in a performance.

The cost of costume and grooming such as hair and makeup incurred by a performer making personal appearances the sole purpose of which is to promote their business activities is also allowable.

A-Z of accountants

BOWKER ORFORD
BASED IN: LONDON
{T} 020 7636 6391
MAIL@BOWKERORFORD.COM
WWW.BOWKERORFORD.COM

We are founder members of the Institute of Chartered Accountants Entertainment and Media Group. We have been acting for clients in the music business for over 30 years and have extensive experience acting on behalf of performers, music publishers and all related areas. As a result we have a good knowledge of copyright, royalty accounting and tax issues. We have in excess of 500 actors as clients, including many household names, and we act for a number of theatrical production companies and theatrical agents.

BRECKMAN & COMPANY
BASED IN: LONDON
{T} 020 7499 2292
INFO@BRECKMANANDCOMPANY.CO.UK
WWW.BRECKMANANDCOMPANY.CO.UK

Breckman & Company, chartered certified accountants, have specialised in the Arts and Entertainment Industry for over 40 years, for both individuals and companies. We are based in the West End of London, near the heart of Theatreland.

CENTRE STAGE
BASED IN: MANCHESTER
{T} 0161 655 2000
ACCOUNTS@CENTRESTAGE-ACCOUNTANTS.COM
WWW.CENTRESTAGE-ACCOUNTANTS.COM

Centre Stage is a firm of Chartered Accountants specialising in the Entertainment Industry. Our experience over many years has led us to believe that there is a need for the kind of specialism we can offer due to the many unusual aspects of the entertainment industry. For example, many actors hold down other jobs, many temporary, often during or between acting jobs, but are treated as self-employed.

DAVID EVANS CHARTERED ACCOUNTANTS
BASED IN: NORTH WEST
{T} 01200 428460
DAVID@EVANSACCOUNTANTS.COM
WWW.EVANSACCOUNTANTS.COM

David Evans Chartered Accountants has acted for individuals and businesses involved in creative work, as well as charities involved in community arts, for over 10 years. We have a wealth of experience and expertise.

GOLDWINS
BASED IN: LONDON
{T} 020 7372 6494
INFO@GOLDWINS.CO.UK
WWW.GOLDWINS.CO.UK

For many years, we have been successfully

offering specialist accounting, taxation and financial services to people in the entertainment professions right across the UK.

INDIGO
BASED IN: SUSSEX
{T} 01403 892683
INFO@INDIGOTAX.COM
WWW.INDIGOTAX.COM

At Indigo we have clients from a wide spectrum of industries. However, we pride ourselves on our knowledge of accountancy in the music or entertainment industry and many of our clients are musicians, performers, producers, writers or are otherwise involved in multimedia business.

MARK CARR & CO
BASED IN: HOVE AND LONDON
{T} 01273 778802 AND 020 7717 8474
INFO@MARKCARR.CO.UK
WWW.MARKCARR.CO.UK

Our principal expertise is supplying accounting and taxation services to the entertainment industry. We act for actors, dancers, writers and agents among other professions within the industry.

MARTIN GREENE
BASED IN: LONDON
{T} 020 7625 4545
MGR@MGR.CO.UK
WWW.MGR.CO.UK

As with all aspects of the entertainment industry, we work closely with lawyers on all contractual, tax planning and commercial matters. These include intellectual property exploitation and protection, recording and licensing contracts.

MGI MIDGLEY SNELLING
BASED IN: LONDON & WEYBRIDGE
{T} 020 7836 9671 & 01932 853 393
EMAIL@MIDSNELL.CO.UK
WWW.MIDSNELL.CO.UK

Since our formation, we have built a strong tradition of delivering specialist services to clients associated with the entertainment industry and have a thorough knowledge and understanding of this unique industry.

SAFFERY CHAMPNESS
BASED IN: LONDON
{T} 020 7841 4000
INFO@SAFFERY.COM
WWW.SAFFERY.COM

Our specialist media and entertainment team act as enthusiastic and trusted advisers to the creative industries sector, to both businesses and individuals operating within it. The group possesses particular experience in the fields of advertising, marketing and PR, film and broadcasting, music, publishing, sport, theatres, and talent agencies.

SLOANE & CO
BASED IN: LONDON
{T} 020 7221 3292
MAIL@SLOANEANDCO.COM
WWW.SLOANE.CO.UK

Sloane & Co., founded in 1974 by David Sloane, is a firm of Accountants offering a wide range of financial services of particular concern to organisations and individuals working in the entertainment field.

Taylorcocks (Bournemouth)
Based in: Bournemouth
{T} 0370 770 8111
BOURNEMOUTHENQUIRIES@THEACCOUNTANTS.CO.UK
WWW.THEACCOUNTANTS.CO.UK
For many years we have provided specialist accounting, taxation, business and financial advice to the leisure and entertainment industry. Our knowledge and experience mean that we understand the special requirements of the sector.

Taylorcocks (Farnham)
Based in: Farnham
{T} 0370 770 8111
FARNHAMENQUIRIES@THEACCOUNTANTS.CO.UK

Taylorcocks (London - Fulham)
Based in: London - Fulham
{T} 0370 770 8111

Taylorcocks (London - Soho)
Based in: London - Soho
{T} 0370 770 8111

Taylorcocks (Portsmouth)
Based in: Portsmouth
{T} 0370 770 8111
PORTSMOUTHENQUIRIES@THEACCOUNTANTS.CO.UK

Taylorcocks (Oxford)
Based in: Oxford
{T} 0370 770 8111
OXFORDENQUIRIES@THEACCOUNTANTS.CO.UK

Taylorcocks (Reading)
Based in: Reading
{T} 0370 770 8111
READINGENQUIRIES@THEACCOUNTANTS.CO.UK

Taylorcocks (Southampton)
Based in: Southampton
{T} 0370 770 8111
SOUTHAMPTONENQUIRIES@THEACCOUNTANTS.CO.UK

TWD Accountants
WWW.TWDACCOUNTS.CO.UK
[T] 0800 093 9433
TWD Accountants is one of the UK's leading low cost, fixed fee tax accountancy services. With over 30 years experience in practice we provide advice and guidelines to help actors and sole traders find their way through the UK tax maze. As well as helping many actors with their personal tax issues, we secure tax refunds and carry out tax health-checks. Our 90 strong team of qualified accountants and senior ex-Revenue staff offer a nationwide service with clients spread through out the UK. In most cases, our unique systems mean there is no need for face to face meetings, which helps maintain lower costs lower and avoiding the need for the soaring hourly charges usually associated with traditional high street accountants

Section 6
Organisations & resources

Equity

Equity, formed in 1930, is the trade union for actors and the entertainment profession. Its 35,000+ members include actors, singers, dancers, choreographers, stage managers, theatre directors and designers, variety and circus artists, television and radio presenters, walk-on and supporting artists, stunt performers and directors and theatre fight directors. Equity works on behalf of actors, lobbying to secure minimum terms and conditions of employment. In addition to its ongoing campaigning for better pay and conditions, Equity offers a casting service, advice and insurance.

To qualify for membership you must have undertaken professional acting work. Subscription fees are 1% of your gross earnings (with a minimum of £125 and a maximum subscription of £2025) plus a one-off £25 joining fee. If you're on a full-time accredited drama course you're eligible for student membership (£15 per year). Outlined below are some of the main benefits of joining Equity (taken from the Equity website).

Pay & conditions
Equity negotiates minimum terms and conditions with employers across all areas of the entertainment industry. Copies of contracts and agreements are available from Equity offices for a small charge.

Help & advice
Equity can help you throughout your career, offering a range of services as well as advice. Its staff have detailed, specialist knowledge and are happy to give advice to members and their agents on contracts and terms of engagement.

Equity card
The universally recognised symbol of your status as a professional in the entertainment industry.

Legal and welfare advice

Free legal advice on disputes over professional engagements including personal injury claims. Free advice on National Insurance, taxation, benefits, pensions and welfare issues.

Publications

A quarterly magazine is sent free of charge to all members, keeping you in touch with Equity initiatives and activities. Equity also produces a wide range of information leaflets which are always available to members.

Medical support

All members can use the British Performing Arts Medicine Trust Helpline to access advice and information on performance-related medical, psychological and dental problems.

Royalties & residuals

Equity distributes royalties, residuals and other payments to members for TV and film re-runs, video sales and sound recordings.

Registers

Equity compiles a large number of specialist registers which are made available to casting directors and employers.

Job information

Equity members can access a service giving them information on job availability across the industry.

Campaigns

Equity campaigns vigorously on behalf of its members on a wide range of national, local and specialist issues and has a strong track record of success.

Your professional name

Equity reserves your choice of professional name when you join, as long as it is not already in use by another member.

Insurance
Public liability of up to £5 million, backstage cover and accident cover are available free to all members as long as they are in benefit. Call First Act Insurance on 020 8686 5050 for more information.

Rights, copyright & new media
Equity monitors national and international developments in intellectual property rights, campaigning for adequate recognition of performers' statutory rights.

Charities
Equity runs two charities, the Equity Benevolent Fund and the Evelyn Norris Trust, which exist to help members in times of trouble. Equity also supports other organisations which provide help specifically for performers.

Pensions
The Equity Pension was set up in 1997 and if a member chooses to join, the BBC, ITV companies, PACT TV companies and West End theatre producers will pay into it when you have a main part with one of them. There is a similar scheme in place for opera singers and dancers in the standing companies.

Discounts
Equity members are entitled to discounts on a range of services and goods including hotels, car breakdown recovery, ticket prices and others.

EQUITY
GUILD HOUSE
UPPER ST MARTINS LANE
LONDON WC2H 9EG
{T} 020 7379 6000
WWW.EQUITY.ORG.UK

Spotlight

Founded in 1927, Spotlight lists more than 30,000 actors and is used by thousands of TV, film, theatre and radio professionals. Once registered you'll appear in The Spotlight Book, published annually, and have an online profile which you can login to with a pin number to keep your details up to date.

Casting professionals can search the online database by a range of characteristics (eg credits, physical attributes and skills). Spotlight is often the first port of call for casting directors and industry professionals whether looking to cast for a particular production or a more general browse and to keep abreast of who is out there, the old hands and the new kids on the block. It is strongly recommended that you join Spotlight – not to do so can be a false economy and entry will ensure that you are in the main 'shop window' for the UK acting profession.

The Spotlight Link is a system which allows industry professionals to post casting breakdowns to registered casting agents who can then submit their clients. Contacts is a directory of industry resources and professionals published by Spotlight. Preliminary application forms can be printed off online or requested by post. Once submitted, these are then vetted. If your application is successful your online entry should appear within 21 days and your profile included in the next available offline directory. You don't need to have an agent but "Spotlight only accepts entries from artists who have recognised training and/or professional acting experience". Costs vary depending on when you join. Please contact Spotlight for current rates.

THE SPOTLIGHT
7 LEICESTER PLACE
LONDON WC2H 7RJ
{T} 020 7437 7631
INFO@SPOTLIGHT.COM
WWW.SPOTLIGHTCD.COM

Casting Call Pro

Established in 2004 and now with 25,000+ professional actors and 15,000+ casting professionals, Casting Call Pro has quickly become one of the largest networking resources for the UK acting industry. Actors can create a comprehensive online profile which displays credits, physical characteristics and skills, photos etc.

Once listed in the directory, actors can be searched and contacted by casting directors. Casting Call Pro employs sophisticated searching and matching technology to provide casting professionals with actors who fit their requirements.

The site also has a section for casting alerts where agents can place character breakdowns. Actors can apply via the site, sending a covering letter direct to the casting director and an automated link to their online Casting Call Pro profile. A tracking system allows them to see when their application has been viewed. This also logs all views from casting professionals searching the directory, giving real time reporting to the actors.

Membership includes entry into the actors' directory, searchable by industry professionals, and access to resources and directories including photographers, theatres, drama schools, networking tools, the agency directory, the employer directory, plays database, film database, substantial discounts on key services (eg headshot sessions for £65 + VAT), and a host of other online resources for the actor.

Minimum requirements for registration
(Members must meet at least one of these criteria)
• training at an NCDT accredited drama school or CDS school
• three professional credits (paid, speaking roles).

Subscription fees

Standard membership gives actors a listing in the directory and is free. The optional premium package allows members to access paid casting alerts, upload up to 20 photographs, showreel and voicereel clips, create a castingcallpro email address (eg mattbarnes@casting-callpro.com) and their own URL (web address). Please contact them for current rates.

Casting Call Pro
Unit 1, Waterloo Gardens
Milner Square
London N1 1TY
{t} 020 7700 0474
info@castingcallpro.com
www.uk.castingcallpro.com

A-Z of useful organisations

THE ACTORS' SOCIETY
WWW.THEACTORSSOCIETY.COM
CONTACT: ANNAMEKA PORTER-SINCLAIR
ANNAMEKA@THEACTORSSOCIETY.COM
The Actors' Society runs seminars throughout the year to help the working actor in their career development. Our exclusive seminars connect the actor with the industry in an atmosphere designed to educate, inspire and empower. Each session is led by an industry expert who offers first hand support and advice.

ACTORS' BENEVOLENT FUND
6 ADAM STREET
LONDON WC2N 6AD
{T} 020 7836 6378
{F} 020 7836 8978
OFFICE@ABF.ORG.UK
WWW2.ACTORSBENEVOLENTFUND.CO.UK
The role of the Actors' Benevolent Fund is to care for actors and theatrical stage managers unable to work because of poor health, an accident or frail old age. The fund has been in place for over 120 years.

ACTORS' CHARITABLE TRUST
58 BLOOMSBURY STREET
LONDON WC1B 3QT
{T} 020 7636 7868
ROBERT@TACTACTORS.ORG
WWW.TACTACTORS.ORG

TACT helps the children of actors under the age of 21 with grants, advice and support.

ACTOREXPO
INFO@ACTOREXPO.CO.UK
WWW.ACTOREXPO.CO.UK
ActorExpo is the UK's biggest trade show dedicated to advancing the careers of actors and performers. Due to its popularity the event has expanded and now takes place in both London and Edinburgh on an annual basis. The show is a unique opportunity for actors and performers to get insider knowledge from experts and to essential practical career advice. The Expo offers: educational programmes, keynote speakers, live performances plus plenty of networking opportunities.

AGENTS' ASSOCIATION
54 KEYES HOUSE
DOLPHIN SQUARE
LONDON SW1V 3NA
{T} 020 7834 0515
{F} 020 7821 0261
ASSOCIATION@AGENTS-UK.COM
WWW.AGENTS-UK.COM
The largest professional trade organisation of its kind in the world. Our member agents represent and book all kinds of performers, celebrities and musicians within all areas of the light entertainment industry.

ARTSLINE
c/o 21 PINE COURT
WOOD LODGE GARDENS
BROMLEY BR 21 2WA
{T} 020 7388 2227
{F} 020 7383 2653
CEO@ARTSLINE.ORG.UK
WWW.ARTSLINE.ORG.UK
Artsline is a disabled led charity
established twenty-five years ago to
promote access for disabled people to
arts and entertainment venues
promoting the clear message that access
equals inclusion.

BECTU
373-377 CLAPHAM ROAD
LONDON SW9 9BT
{T} 020 7346 0900
{F} 020 7346 0901
INFO@BECTU.ORG.UK
WWW.BECTU.ORG.UK
BECTU is the independent union for
those working in broadcasting, film,
theatre, entertainment, leisure,
interactive media and allied areas. The
union represents permanently employed,
contract and freelance workers who are
primarily based in the United Kingdom.

BRITISH ACADEMY OF DRAMATIC COMBAT
3 CASTLE VIEW
HELMSLEY
NORTH YORKS YO62 5AU
WORKSHOPCOORDINATOR@BADC.CO.UK
WWW.BADC.CO.UK
The BADC is the longest established

stage combat teaching organization in
the United Kingdom. The BADC also
enjoys international recognition as a
provider of excellence in teaching
quality, curriculum design and
assessment rigour. The BADC is
dedicated to the advance of the art of
stage combat in all forms of
performance media.

BRITISH ARTS FESTIVAL ASSOCIATION
1 GOODWINS COURT
LONDON WC2N 4LL
{T} 020 7240 4532
INFO@ARTSFESTIVALS.CO.UK
WWW.ARTSFESTIVALS.CO.UK
BAFA is a vibrant membership organisa-
tion covering the widest span of arts
festivals in the UK. These include some
of the large international cultural events
such as the Edinburgh International
Festival and Brighton Festival through to
small dynamic festivals such as the
Winchester Hat Fair and the Corsham
Festival in Wiltshire.

BRITISH COUNCIL
BRIDGEWATER HOUSE
58 WHITWORTH STREET
MANCHESTER M1 6BB
{T} 0161 957 7755
GENERAL.ENQUIRIES@BRITISHCOUNCIL.ORG
WWW.BRITISHCOUNCIL.ORG
The organisation was set up in 1934 to
promote a wider knowledge of the
United Kingdom abroad, to promote the
knowledge of the English language, and

to develop closer cultural relations between the United Kingdom and other countries.

British Film Institute (BFI)
Belvedere Road
South Bank
London SE1 8XT
{T} 020 7928 3535
LIBRARY@BFI.ORG.UK
WWW.BFI.ORG.UK
The BFI promotes understanding and appreciation of Britain's rich film and television heritage and culture.

Casting Directors Guild
{T} 020 8741 1951
WWW.THECDG.CO.UK
The Guild is a professional organisation of casting directors in the film, television, theatre and commercials communities in the UK who have joined together to further their common interests in establishing a recognised standard of professionalism in the industry, enhancing the stature of the profession, providing a free exchange of information and ideas, honouring the achievements of members and standardisation of working practices within the industry.

Co-operative Personal Management Association
WWW.CPMA.MOONFRUIT.COM
Founded in 2002, the CPMA works to further and promote the interests of its members, who are acting agencies located across the UK. Backed by Equity, the CPMA seeks to raise the profile of co-ops with both employers and actors and to represent the interests of co-ops with external bodies. They also work with their members to identify and assist in solving the unique problems of a co-op, to encourage good business practice, to develop training skills and opportunites, and to act as an advocate for co-operative working.

Conference of Drama Schools (CDS)
The Executive Secretary
PO BOX 34252
London NW5 1XJ
INFO@CDS.DRAMA.AC.UK
WWW.DRAMA.AC.UK
The Conference of Drama Schools comprises Britain's 22 leading drama schools. CDS exists in order to strengthen the voice of the member schools, to set and maintain the highest standards of training within the vocational drama sector, and to make it easier for prospective students to understand the range of courses on offer and the application process. Founded in 1969, the 22 member schools offer courses in acting, musical theatre, directing and technical theatre training.

Conservatoire for Dance and Drama (CDD)

Tavistock House
Tavistock Square
London WC1H 9JJ
{T} 020 7387 5101
INFO@CDD.AC.UK
WWW.CDD.AC.UK

The Conservatoire for Dance and Drama (CDD) is a new higher education institution, founded in 2001. It was established to protect and promote some of the best schools offering vocational training in dance, drama and circus arts. The CDD offers courses in acting, stage management, classical ballet, theatre directing, contemporary dance, lighting, costume and scenic design. Entry to the schools is very competitive but they seek students who have the talent, skill and determination to succeed regardless of their background.

Council for Dance Education and Training (CDET)

Old Brewer's Yard
17-19 Neal Street
London WC2H 9UY
{T} 020 7240 5703
INFO@CDET.ORG.UK
WWW.CDET.ORG.UK

Founded in 1979, the Council for Dance Education and Training is the national standards body of the professional dance industry. It accredits programmes of training in vocational dance schools

and holds the Register of Dance Awarding Bodies – the directory of teaching societies whose syllabuses have been inspected and approved by the Council. It is the body of advocacy of the dance education and training communities and offers a free and comprehensive information service, Answers for Dancers, on all aspects of vocational dance provision to students, parents, teachers dance artists and employers.

Drama Association of Wales

The Old Library, Singleton Road
Splott
Cardiff CF24 2ET
{T} 029 2045 2200
INFO@DRAMAWALES.ORG.UK
WWW.DRAMAWALES.ORG.UK

Founded in 1934 and a registered charity since 1973, the Association offers a wide and varied range of services to Community Drama. Among others, members include amateur and professional theatre practitioners, educationalists and playwrights.

The Drama Student Magazine

Top Floor
66 Wansey Street
London SE17 1JP
{T} 020 7701 4536
EDITOR@THEDRAMASTUDENT.CO.UK
WWW.THEDRAMASTUDENT.CO.UK

The Drama Student Magazine launched in January 2009 as the first and only publication dedicated to drama students in the UK. Covering the entire journey, from auditioning for vocation training, right through to graduation, each quarterly issue is packed with inspiring interviews, articles and news that are sure to assist students in their chosen career path. Embarking on a career in the industry as an actor or behind the scenes is an exciting time and The Drama Student aims to be at the forefront of that passion, delivering a publication with enthusiasm and substance.

FOUNDATION FOR COMMUNITY DANCE
LCB DEPOT
31 RUTLAND STREET
LEICESTER LE1 1RE
{T} 0116 253 3453
INFO@COMMUNITYDANCE.ORG.UK
WWW.COMMUNITYDANCE.ORG.UK
The Foundation for Community Dance is a UK-wide charity, established in 1986, to support the development of community dance, providing information, advice and guidance for dance artists, organisations, students and communities about community dance and the issues they face.

FRINGE THEATRE NETWORK
IMEX BUSINESS CENTRE
INGATE PLACE
LONDON SW8 3NS
{T} 020 7627 4920
HELENOLDREDLION@YAHOO.CO.UK
WWW.FRINGETHEATRE.ORG.UK

Fringe Theatre Network (FTN) was founded in 1986 as Pub Theatre Network when fringe venues felt the need for an organisation to support them, keep them in touch with each other and present their case on their behalf. FTN was registered as a charity in 1987 and exists to support and promote fringe theatre in London by providing services, support and a network of contacts for venues, producing companies and individuals working on the fringe and thereby to increase the viability and profession-alism of fringe theatre, and by repre-senting fringe theatre as an umbrella organisation which can act and speak on behalf of fringe theatre to statutory authorities, funding bodies, policy makers and other arts organisations.

INDEPENDENT THEATRE COUNCIL (ITC)
12 THE LEATHERMARKET
WESTON STREET
LONDON SE1 3ER
{T} 020 7403 1727
ADMIN@ITC-ARTS.ORG
WWW.ITC-ARTS.ORG
The ITC is the UK's leading management association for the performing arts, rep-resenting around 700 organisations across the country. The ITC works closely with Equity on agreements, contracts and rights for performers.

\

**NATIONAL ASSOCIATION OF
YOUTH THEATRES**
DARLINGTON ARTS CENTRE
VANE TERRACE
DARLINGTON DL3 7AX
{T} 01325 363330
{F} 01325 363313
NAYTUK@BTCONNECT.COM
WWW.NAYT.ORG.UK
NAYT (National Association of Youth Theatres) supports the development of youth theatre activity through training, advocacy, participation programmes and information services.

**NATIONAL COUNCIL FOR DRAMA TRAINING
(NCDT)**
249 TOOLEY STREET
LONDON SE1 2JX
{T} 020 7407 3686
INFO@NCDT.CO.UK
WWW.NCDT.CO.UK
The National Council for Drama Training is a partnership of employers in theatre, broadcast and media industries, employee representatives and training providers. The aim of the COUNCIL is to act as a champion for the drama industry, working to optimise support for professional drama training and education, embracing change and development.

**NATIONAL OPERATIC AND DRAMATIC
ASSOCIATION (NODA)**
58-60 LINCOLN ROAD
PETERBOROUGH PE1 2RZ
INFO@NODA.ORG.UK
WWW.NODA.ORG.UK
The National Operatic and Dramatic Association (NODA), founded in 1899, is the main representative body for amateur theatre in the UK. It has a membership of some 2500 amateur/community theatre groups and 3000 individual enthusiasts throughout the UK, staging musicals, operas, plays, concerts and pantomimes in a wide variety of performing venues, ranging from the country's leading professional theatres to village halls.

NATIONAL YOUTH THEATRE
443-445 HOLLOWAY ROAD
LONDON N7 6LW
{T} 020 7281 3863
INFO@NYT.ORG.UK
WWW.NYT.ORG.UK
The National Youth Theatre was established in 1956 to offer young people the chance to develop their creative and social skills through the medium of the theatrical arts which includes acting and technical disciplines. The National Youth Theatre is now an internationally acclaimed organisation, providing opportunities to all young people aged 13-21 in the UK, regardless of background.

PERFORMING RIGHTS SOCIETY
COPYRIGHT HOUSE
29-33 BERNERS ST
LONDON W1T 3AB
WWW.PRSFOR MUSIC.COM
[T] 020 7580 5544

PERSONAL MANAGERS ASSOCIATION (PMA)
PO BOX 63819
LONDON N1P 1HL
{T} 0845 6027191
INFO@THEPMA.COM
WWW.THEPMA.COM

The PMA is the professional association of agents representing UK based actors, writers, producers, directors, designers and technicians in the film, television and theatre industries. Established in 1950 as the Personal Managers' Association, the PMA has over 130 member agencies representing more than 1,000 agents.

NORTHERN ACTORS CENTRE
21-31 OLDHAM STREET
MANCHESTER M1 1JG
{T} 0161 819 2513
INFO@ACTORSCENTRENORTH.COM
WWW.ACTORSCENTRENORTH.COM

The NAC provides workshops for actors and other professionals in theatre, television, film and radio to enable them to continuously maintain and develop their craft once their initial training has been completed. Areas covered include physical, vocal, studio techniques, char-acterisation, approaches to specific styles, genres and authors, career management.

SHOOTING PEOPLE
HTTPS://SHOOTINGPEOPLE.ORG

Shooting People is a community of 37,000+ filmmakers who share their resources, skills and experience. Members post to and receive up to eight daily email bulletins, which cover all aspects of filmmaking; add their events and screenings to the Indie Film calendars; and network with other members at parties, salons and screenings in London, New York and beyond; create dynamic, online searchable profile cards; and upload their films and reels to the site.

SKILLSET
FOCUS POINT
21 CALEDONIAN ROAD
LONDON N1 9GB
{T} 020 7713 9800
INFO@SKILLSET.ORG
WWW.SKILLSET.ORG

Skillset is the Sector Skills Council for the audiovisual industries (broadcast, film, video, interactive media and photo imaging). They conduct consultation work with industry, publish research and strategic documents, run funding schemes and project work, and provide information about the challenges that face the industry. They also provide impartial media careers advice for aspiring new entrants and established industry professionals, online, face to face and over the phone.

Society of Teachers of Speech & Drama

73 Berry Hill Road
Mansfield
Nottinghamshire NG18 4RU
{T} 01623 627636
STSD@STSD.ORG.UK
WWW.STSD.ORG.UK

The STSD was established soon after the Second World War from the amalgamation of two much earlier Associations formed to protect the professional interests of qualified, specialist teachers of speech and drama, to encourage good standards of teaching and to promote the study and knowledge of speech and dramatic art in every form.

Theatrical Management Association (TMA)

32 Rose Street
London WC2E 9ET
{T} 020 7557 6700
{F} 020 7557 6799
ENQUIRIES@SOLTTMA.CO.UK
WWW.TMAUK.ORG

TMA is the pre-eminent UK wide organisation dedicated to providing professional support for the performing arts. Members include repertory and producing theatres, arts centres and touring venues, major national companies and independent producers, opera and dance companies and associated businesses. The association undertakes advocacy on behalf of members to authorities to promote the value of investment in the performing arts. The association also facilitates facilitating concerted action to promote theatre-going to the widest possible audience.

Women in Film and Television (WFTV)

[T] 020 7287 1400
INFO@WFTV.ORG.UK
WWW.WFTV.ORG.UK

Women in Film & TV is the premier membership organisation for women working in creative media in the UK, and part of an international network of over 10,000 women worldwide. Members of the organisation come from a broad range of professions spanning the entire creative media industry. WFTV host a variety of events throughout the year, present a glamorous awards ceremony every December, and run a mentoring programme for women in the industry. They also host networking evenings, collaborate with industry bodies on research projects and lobby for women's interests.

General index